GREAT EVENTS
IN THE LIFE OF
GENERAL CUSTER

...comes General McClellan's aide,
with rank of captain, 1862

6 Is promoted to Brigadier General
of Volunteers, 1863

...court-martialed for disobeying orders
during Indian campaign, 1867

7 Marries Elizabeth Bacon in
Monroe, Michigan, 1864

THE STORY OF
General Custer

Soldiers and horses were killed all around him

THE STORY OF
General Custer

By MARGARET LEIGHTON

Illustrated by NICHOLAS EGGENHOFER

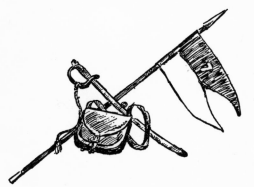

ENID LAMONTE MEADOWCROFT
Supervising Editor

PUBLISHERS Grosset & Dunlap NEW YORK

PRINTED IN THE UNITED STATES OF AMERICA

Library of Congress Catalog Card No. 54–5858

This book is dedicated to
LEIGHTON, JOEL,
and BRUCE

Contents

[*vii*]

CONTENTS

Illustrations

[*ix*]

ILLUSTRATIONS

THE STORY OF
General Custer

"I'm going to be a general," Autie said

CHAPTER I

The Blacksmith's Shop

CLANG-CLINK! Clang-clink! Clang-clink!

Autie Custer sat up in bed and looked about him sleepily. He saw the sun streaming in through the small panes of the bedroom window. A little breeze stirred the crisp white curtains. The big four-poster bed beside his own small trundle bed was empty.

"Pa and Ma are already up," he thought. "I guess breakfast's ready."

Then the noise came again. Clang-clink! Clang-clink! Now Autie was wide awake, and he remembered the plan he had made the night before. Quickly he jumped out of bed. He pulled on his trousers and stuffed his shirt

[3]

down inside them. Then he ran, barefooted, down the stairs. Without stopping for breakfast he hurried out of doors and around the house to his father's blacksmith shop.

A man Autie did not know was standing in the doorway of the smithy. Autie thought he must be the owner of the big bay horse which was tied there, waiting to be shod.

The inside of the blacksmith shop seemed dark after the bright sunshine. But in a moment Autie could see his father, Emmanuel Custer, working at the anvil in his heavy leather apron. His older half brother, Brice, stood at the forge. He was pulling the big bellows, making the fire burn brightly through the shadows.

"Hello, Autie," Brice said. Then he spoke sharply. "Keep away from that horse's heels, Autie!" he warned.

But Autie ran across the smithy, heedless of the horse or anything else. The big bay laid back his ears and shied a little as he passed.

"Pa!" Autie cried. "Pa, I want you to make something for me. Will you, Pa?"

Emmanuel Custer looked up from his work. "Can't you see I'm busy shoeing this gentleman's horse, Autie? Don't bother me now," he said. But he smiled at his small son as he spoke.

He held a glowing, red-hot horseshoe on the anvil with a pair of long tongs. And now the sharp, ringing sound which had waked Autie came again. Clang-clink! Clang-clink! Clang-clink! Sparks flew like Fourth of July fireworks as the smith's great, heavy hammer beat on the iron.

"But, Pa!" Autie's voice rose shrilly. "Pa, I *want* you to make me a sword. Not a wooden sword, but a real iron one, like real soldiers use. Make it now so I can carry it when I go drilling this afternoon with you and the other soldiers."

But his father just turned the horseshoe over and continued his work without answering. Autie began to jump up and down impatiently.

"Pa, go on, say you will. Say you'll make me a real iron sword to fight with!" he demanded.

"Whom are you planning to fight, sonny?" the stranger asked from the doorway.

"Injuns," Autie told him promptly.

"Have you got any Injuns here in New Rumley?" the man asked. "We haven't had any

[5]

where I live, in Cadiz, not for a long time. I don't think you'll find one in all of Harrison County, unless there's a few that have settled down to live like white men. This is 1843, boy. Ohio ain't backwoods any more. You can take my word for that."

Autie's father nodded. "That's right, Mr. Turner. What's more, son, you've got that little wooden gun I made for you. What do you want a sword for? Guns are lots more use than swords. Any soldier'll tell you that."

"But generals carry swords, and I want to be a general," Autie explained.

The stranger threw back his head and laughed loudly. Brice laughed, too, and Emmanuel Custer chuckled.

"It takes a long time to learn how to be a general, son," he said. "Years and years. You've got to practice being a real good soldier first."

"Well, I'm going to be one, anyway," Autie said. His cheeks were red and he nodded his yellow, curly head decidedly. "I'm going to be a general and ride a big horse and carry a big sword."

"When you get to be a general you can have

a sword, sure enough," his father told him. "But not today. Your ma made you that fine little uniform and I made you your gun. That'll have to satisfy you. Now hush this hollering and mind your manners. Say howdy to Mr. Turner, here. Mr. Turner, meet my boy, George Armstrong Custer. He'll be five next birthday. We call him Autie for short."

"You're a big boy for your age, Autie," Mr. Turner said, as they shook hands.

"What's your horse's name, Mr. Turner?" Autie asked. "He looks like he could go fast."

"His name's Duke and he is a pretty fast stepper," the man said. "Do you like horses, Autie?"

Autie nodded again. "Yes, *sir!*" he said. "I can ride, too."

"Is that a fact?" Mr. Turner's eyes twinkled as he spoke. "Looks to me like your legs are pretty short to straddle a horse."

"He can, though," Brice spoke up quickly. "Autie can stick on a horse real good. He's not afraid of anything."

Autie grinned and stood as straight and tall as he could. He liked to hear nice things about himself. He knew already that his older broth-

[7]

ers and sisters were extra fond and proud of him. He had heard people say that they spoiled him terribly.

"I hear you've got quite a family now, Mr. Custer," Mr. Turner said.

"Yes, that's right," Emmanuel Custer agreed. "My wife was a widow and I was a widower when we married. We already had three children apiece. That gave us six to begin with. Now we've two more—this little towhead, Autie—the liveliest of the lot. And his baby brother, Nevin."

He gave a few final blows to the horseshoe. Then he plunged it for a moment into the tub of water which stood beside the anvil. Steam rose in a hissing cloud as the hot iron touched the water.

"Now we'll see how this goes," he said. "All right, Duke, old fellow. Just stand easy."

He lifted the horse's foot and held it between his knees on his leather apron. There was a queer, scorched smell as he fitted the still-hot iron to the hoof.

Duke could not feel the heat, but he rolled his eyes nervously. His owner patted his arched neck soothingly and then he stood still. Brice brought the horsehair fly whisk. Whenever a cruel, green-headed horsefly lighted on Duke's shining coat, Brice flicked it off in short order.

Autie came closer. He loved to watch his father's big hands working so skillfully at his

trade. Each nail had to be set in a hole in the iron shoe, then pounded through the hard edge of the hoof.

Mr. Turner watched the work approvingly.

"So you find time to drill with the militia, along with all your other jobs, Mr. Custer?" he said. "I've heard of the New Rumley Militia. The New Rumley Invincibles, folks call them. That's quite a name!"

Autie's father chuckled as he clinched the final horseshoe nail. "Names don't cost anything. We figured we might as well choose a good one while we were about it," he said.

"Well, maybe you'll have to live up to that name if we ever have war with Mexico," Mr. Turner continued. "It looks as though we might."

Mr. Custer's face grew sober. "I hope we won't go to war," he said. "Of course, I believe our country should be able and ready to stand up for her rights. But I'm a man of peace. I—"

A shrill, high-pitched voice interrupted them. Both men turned. Autie stood balanced on top of the big anvil. He held his father's long tongs uplifted like a sword. "My voice is for war!" he cried. He was repeating the words of a speech he had heard his older brother recite in a school contest. "My voice is for war!" he shouted again.

Autie saw his father and Mr. Turner and

Brice all staring at him with their mouths open in surprise. He began to think that he was doing something very clever indeed.

"*My* voice—" he cried again, flourishing the tongs above his head.

Then his foot slipped. The next instant he landed with a splash in the big tub half full of cold, dirty water.

His father fished him out, and Autie stood sputtering and coughing. Everyone was laughing at him. Even Lydia was laughing—Lydia, his best-loved older sister. She had arrived just in time to see his downfall.

Then Autie himself began to laugh. He was still laughing gaily when Lydia rolled him up in her apron and lifted him into her arms.

"Come along and get some dry clothes and eat your breakfast, little show-off," she said, carrying the future general back to the house.

CHAPTER II

Two Boys and an Apple Orchard

"W<small>AIT</small> a minute, Autie. *You* carry the
lunch pail for a while," Nevin Custer called to
his older brother. "It's heavy and I'm getting
hot."

Autie was now twelve years old. He and two
of his younger brothers, Nevin and Tom, were
on their way to school. They no longer lived in
the village of New Rumley. Their father had
moved his blacksmith shop to a farm on the
border of the township. The Custer children
had a long walk to and from school each day.
And it was warm—much too warm for October.

As usual, Autie led the way. Tommy trotted
close at his heels while Nevin plodded behind.

Their bare feet made little puffs in the dust of the road at every step.

Autie paused and waited for Nevin to catch up. All three boys had left home with clean clothes, well-scrubbed faces, and smoothly brushed hair. But now Tommy had smudges and stains on his face and shirt from eating late blackberries. And the breeze had stirred Autie's yellow hair into a tangle of curls.

"Hurry up," Autie said impatiently. Just as he spoke the clang of the school bell came to them on the bright, windy air.

"We're late!" Nevin cried, and he began to run.

But instead of running, Autie stood stock still. "I'm not going to school, after all," he announced. "It's too nice outdoors. I don't want to be cooped up in that stuffy old schoolroom. Let's play hookey."

"Teacher'll give us a whipping if we do," Nevin reminded him. "I don't want to be whipped. I'm going on."

"His whippings don't hurt *me!*" Autie said. "But go on if you're scared."

"I'm going with Autie," said little Tom. "*I'm* not scared. And Autie's always fun."

[*14*]

"Well, I've got the lunch, anyway," Nevin answered, and off he sped.

"He's got *our* lunch!" Tom wailed, as he watched his brother disappear round a bend in the road.

"We'll get something better to eat," Autie told him. "We'll go to old Jake Sands' orchard and pick us some apples. Then we'll go and climb Pinnacle Rock. How'd you like that?"

"Oh, I'd like that fine," Tom cried joyfully. "You always think of exciting things to do, Autie."

The two boys turned back along the road.

"Let's cut through the woods so nobody'll see us," Autie suggested. Suddenly he stopped again. "Listen. Do you hear a team coming?"

The sound grew louder. "It's coming fast," Tommy said.

"It's the morning stagecoach!" Autie cried. "Let's hide and watch it go by."

They jumped into the tall weeds beside the road and crouched low. The noise of pounding hoofs came nearer. Now they could hear the rattle of wheels, too. Soon four horses rounded the turn in the road, drawing a high, flat-topped coach behind them.

[*15*]

Dust boiled up in clouds behind the whirling wheels as the stage sped past, rocking, swaying, and creaking.

Tommy stood erect among the big burdock leaves to gaze after it. "My, but I'd like to ride in that. Wouldn't you, Autie?" he asked.

"Sure. But I'd rather ride on one of those new railroad cars behind a steam engine! I saw a lot of them going along their iron tracks when I went to visit Lydia."

He smiled when he thought of his sister, Lydia. Two years before, she had married David Reed and gone to live in Monroe, Michigan. They had invited Autie to come to see them and he had stayed there for a good long visit.

When he came home again, the farm had seemed dull and tame after life in the busy town on the shores of Lake Erie. And how he missed Lydia! She was so cheerful and full of fun, and she had always been like a second mother to him.

But now Tommy was tugging at his arm. "What'll we do now, Autie?" he was asking.

"We'll go get those apples from Jake Sands' orchard, that's what," Autie said. "Come along."

They crossed a stubble field, then plunged into a thick wood. Tommy needed all his breath to keep up with his brother and to fight his way through the tangled underbrush. "What if we get lost in here, Autie?" he gasped. "Do you s'pose there are any wildcats or—or bears in these woods?"

Autie laughed. "You just stick close to me, Tom, and you'll be all right," he said. "I've

[*17*]

never got lost in my life. I can always find my way in any woods."

Suddenly they left the shadowy woods and came into bright sunlight again. Beyond a rail fence lay the apple orchard. Ripe red fruit shone temptingly through the thinning leaves.

"I hope old man Sands isn't anywhere near," Tommy whispered. "He said he'd take his buggy whip to any boys he caught stealing his apples. I heard him tell Pa that."

"He'll have to catch us, first," Autie said, grinning. "Come on."

They scrambled over the fence. Autie climbed one of the trees and shook down a shower of apples. There were more than enough to fill all their pockets and the fronts of their shirts, besides.

"These sure are good!" Tommy said, his mouth full.

"Look there!" Autie cried. "Over in the pasture beyond the fence. There's the sorrel colt old Sands was bragging about. He's not broken to ride yet. Old Sands says he's the finest two-year-old in the county."

As though he heard and understood what the boy was saying, the young horse lifted his head. He gazed at Autie, his ears pointed forward. Then he came trotting up to the fence. He put his head over the rails and whinnied.

"Maybe he'd like an apple," Tommy said. "Can I give him one, Autie?"

"Sure!" Autie said. His blue eyes began to sparkle and his cheeks flushed red. "You start feeding him the apple. *I'm* going to ride him!"

From the top rail of the fence it was easy for Autie to slip over on to the shining, glossy

[*19*]

back. The colt gave a start when the boy's weight touched him. For a moment he stood still, as though he did not realize what had happened.

Autie took a firm hold on the mane and gripped with his knees. He felt the animal's muscles gather under him. Then the young horse leaped forward and began to run.

"Autie!" Tommy shouted in terror.

But Autie himself felt no fear at all. All that he felt was excitement and wild, thrilling joy as the wind whistled past his ears. "Yea-ay!" he shouted, his voice high and shrill. "Go it, boy! Go it!"

Faster and faster the colt ran, round and round the pasture, while the boy clung like a lizard to his back. Autie had a glimpse of Tommy leaning through the fence. Tom's face was screwed up and his mouth was wide open as though he were crying.

Now the colt began to kick and buck, trying to shake off the strange weight on his back. Autie clung stubbornly, but the colt was getting frightened.

Suddenly the horse stopped short, put his head down, and kicked his heels high into the air. Autie's grip was broken and off he sailed. He landed with a thud on the short pasture grass—a thud that knocked the wind clean out of him.

For a moment he lay there, too dizzy to move, trying to collect his thoughts. Then he saw that two people were bending over him. One was Tommy, and the other—the other was Jake Sands!

"Are you hurt, boy?" There was real worry on the old man's face. "Don't move for a minute. Better make sure no bones are broken."

Autie sat up, grinning. "I'm all right," he said. "That sure is a fine horse of yours, Mr. Sands. Best I ever rode."

Now Mr. Sands didn't look worried any more. He looked angry. "Yes, he *is* a fine horse. Lots too good for a crazy boy to ruin by reckless riding," he said sternly.

He jerked Autie to his feet. "I'm glad you aren't hurt. But now I'm going to march you and your little brother home to your pa. If he's the man I think he is, you'll get what you deserve from him! And he hustled the two boys home.

Late that night, when Autie and Tom were asleep, Emmanuel and Maria Custer sat before the fire, talking.

"What did Autie have to say for himself when you whipped him?" Autie's mother asked.

"Well," Emmanuel Custer answered, "as usual, he was ashamed and sorry. But I'm afraid he'll forget all about the whipping the next time he wants to do something rash and foolish. That boy doesn't know what danger means."

"No. Autie's fearless as a lion," Maria

[22]

agreed. "I really worry more about little Tom. Autie never seems to get hurt, but Tom follows him everywhere and tries to do everything he does. I can't watch Tommy all the time with baby Boston to look after."

Mr. Custer put his arm affectionately about his wife. "I know you have your hands full. Perhaps it would be wise to send Autie back to Lydia for a while. His teacher complains that although the boy is quick and bright, he's idle and won't study. In our one-room school, where all the grades are together, the teacher doesn't have time to keep him at his work. Shall we send him to Lydia?"

Maria's worried frown cleared. "That might be best," she agreed. "Lydia writes that Boyd's Seminary, in Monroe, is a real good, up-to-date school. Maybe the teachers there can make our wild, reckless boy behave."

CHAPTER III

Autie Makes Up His Mind

THE journey to Monroe, Michigan, was tiresome and difficult in the year 1851. Most travelers dreaded the long days of riding in rocking, jolting, dusty stagecoaches. And the taverns along the way, where they spent the nights, were usually poorly furnished and uncomfortable.

But Autie Custer was eager and excited when he climbed aboard the coach on that first morning. Hadn't he made the journey two years before? He felt like a seasoned traveler. He said good-by cheerfully to his family, who had gathered in the village street to see him off.

His yellow hair shone in the morning sun as he leaned out of the window to wave. "Good-by, good-by!" he shouted again.

The fresh horses trotted swiftly down the
long slope. Then a turn in the road shut off
Autie's view of the houses on the hilltop. He
drew his head inside and looked with interest
at the other passengers.

There were only three—an elderly gentleman and two women. Before the end of the first day's journey Autie had made friends with all three. The time passed swiftly for him and he slept soundly each night, even though the tavern beds were often uncomfortable.

On the last morning of his journey an old man climbed into the coach with the help of a crutch. One of his trouser legs flapped loosely about a wooden peg.

It wasn't long before Autie had struck up a conversation with the newcomer.

"My name's Marcus Ford," he told the boy. "How far are you going?"

"To Monroe, Michigan," Autie replied. "Have you ever been there?"

"Me? I should say so. Part of me's still there," Ford answered. He gave such a jovial wink that Autie laughed aloud. "I left my leg there during the War. Not the Mexican War. The War of 1812," he added.

"Oh, were you in the army way back then?" Autie cried. "Did you fight the British?"

"Yes, the British and the Injuns," the veteran answered. "I fought in the Battle of Raisin River—the battle we lost."

"But the Americans won the war, didn't they?"

"Sure we won the war, sonny. But some of us was captured by the British and some by the Injuns at Raisin River. Them pesky Injuns killed every man they took, wounded and all."

Autie drew a long breath. "Say, that was bad! Maybe I'll get a chance to pay them back for that, some day. I'm going to be a general, when I grow up."

"A general, eh?" the veteran asked, his eyes twinkling. "Are you fixing to go to West Point?"

"West Point?" Autie repeated. "What's that?"

Ford raised his eyebrows. "Why, that's the big school in New York State, on the Hudson River, where they teach youngsters how to be officers. You can't get to be a general unless you go there. Better start planning for West Point right soon, sonny."

"I sure will!" Autie answered. He was going to ask more, but he noticed that the coach was slowing down. They were already entering Monroe.

[*27*]

The old soldier leaned forward and looked out of the window. "Well, here we are," he said. "There's Judge Bacon's mansion. Finest house for miles around. And there's the judge himself coming down the walk. That's what a *real* gentleman looks like, boy. Top hat, broadcloth coat, gold-headed cane and all!"

But Autie didn't even bother to look at Judge Bacon. His thoughts were far away, in New York State on the Hudson River. "I'll go to West Point," he told himself. "If that's where you learn to be an officer, that's where I'm going to go!"

The stagecoach rolled on through tree-lined streets to the tavern which served as its sta-

tion. As soon as the coach stopped, Autie saw
Lydia and her husband, David Reed, waiting
for him. He said a hurried good-by to Mr.
Ford and jumped out.

Lydia caught him in her arms. "Autie!" she
cried. She hugged him so that he could hardly
breathe. Then she drew back and looked at
him. "Is it really you? I declare, you've grown
so I'd hardly know you. Look, David, he's as
tall as I am," she said.

David Reed didn't hug his young brother-in-law. Instead, he shook his hand, man-fashion. "Of course he's grown, Lydia. What did you expect in two years?" he said teasingly. "You've got a man's grip already, Autie. Let's feel your muscle."

Autie flexed his arm proudly. David felt it, then clapped him on the shoulder. "Solid as a rock! I bet you've been pitching hay."

[*30*]

"That's right," Autie answered. "Brice and I worked all summer in the hay fields."

He picked up his bag. The three started walking along the street toward the Reed home, talking gaily as they went. Yellow autumn leaves lay thick under their feet and the air was bright and cool. How pleasant Monroe looked, and how good it was to see Lydia again, Autie thought.

They passed Judge Bacon's house on their way. It was a fine, big house, set in the midst of lawns and flowers. A little girl was sitting on the white-pillared porch, rocking her doll. But the judge was not in sight.

Soon the three reached the small, pleasant cottage where the Reeds lived.

"I've already enrolled you in Boyd's Seminary, Autie," Lydia said, as they entered. "You'll start school there on Monday. Now promise me that you'll study hard."

"Do you suppose I could learn enough at Boyd's Seminary to get into West Point?" Autie asked.

"West Point?" Lydia exclaimed. She had been untying the strings of her bonnet, and now she stood with it in her hands. "Where on earth did you get an idea like that, Autie?"

"Well, I want to be an army officer, and they say a fellow has to go to West Point to learn how," he explained.

"Does Pa know that you want to go there?" Lydia asked. "Does your mother?"

Autie shook his head. "I just decided today," he answered.

Lydia hung her bonnet on a peg and took off her shawl. "Well, I'm sure Boyd's Seminary could prepare you for West Point if *any* school could," she said. "But not unless you study."

"Then I'll study hard," Autie promised.

It wasn't easy for Autie to keep that promise. He soon learned that to get into West Point he would have to do well in algebra and geometry and other difficult subjects. So he really worked at his lessons.

Somehow he got through the first year at Boyd's Seminary. The second year wasn't quite so difficult, for he had learned how to concentrate on his work. Now he wasn't always at the foot of his class, but he was never at its head, either.

Then spring came, the spring of his second year in Monroe. Autie was walking home from school with his books in a strap over his shoulder. He felt the warm south wind on his face. The smell of wet earth and melting snow made him think of the farm at home in Ohio.

For a moment, getting into West Point did not seem so very important. He longed to be at home again with his family. Then he walked past Judge Bacon's fine white house. A little girl in a pink ruffled dress was swinging on the gate.

She looked up into his face. Her eyes were big and dark, and they sparkled with mischief. "Hello, you Custer boy," she said suddenly.

Autie stopped in surprise. How in the world did she know his name? "Hello. Who are you?" he asked.

"I'm Libbie Bacon," she answered. Then, all at once, she seemed overcome with shyness. She jumped down from the gate and ran up the path to the house.

Autie stood watching her until the door slammed shut behind her. How pretty she was, with her soft, brown curls and her big, long-lashed dark eyes! Judge Bacon's daughter. "Why, she's a regular little princess," he thought. "And she knew *my* name."

[*33*]

He drew a deep, full breath. Then he swung the strapful of books to his shoulder again and walked on briskly down the street, whistling as he went.

"She's the judge's daughter," he thought. "But *I'm* going to be a general!"

CHAPTER IV

The Broken Window

AUTIE CUSTER finished his second year at Boyd's Seminary and even managed to graduate. But he was still a long way from West Point.

"I'll work on Pa's farm this summer," he told Lydia and David, as he said good-by. "Then, next fall, I'm going to teach school. There's a school near New Rumley that needs a teacher and Mr. Boyd has recommended me."

"*You*—teach school?" Lydia cried in amazement. "Why, Autie, you're not sixteen yet."

Autie grinned. "I know. But I'm big for my age, and I look older. I know enough to teach a primary school. I can keep order, too, and that's just as important. Some of the pupils in that school are big rough fellows. They've been making life miserable for other teachers, but I bet *I* can handle them."

"Yes, I'm sure you can!" David agreed.

"I'll get my room and board and twenty-six dollars a month," Autie continued proudly. "It's time I was supporting myself."

"But—" Lydia began, then stopped herself. She had been going to ask, "How about West Point?" She hoped that Autie had changed his mind about becoming an army officer. Lydia knew that his mother did not like the idea. Perhaps she had persuaded him to give up his ambition to be a soldier.

Autie returned to the busy life of a farm summer. He enjoyed the outdoor work, after his months of studying. All the Custer boys, Brice, Autie, Nevin, Tom, and even little Boston, worked from sun-up until evening. They hoed weeds and fed the stock. They milked, and built and repaired fences. They pitched hay and chopped wood for the kitchen stove.

The big, growing boys seemed always hungry.

"I declare, Autie, I don't see how you can hold so much!" his mother exclaimed as they sat at dinner one day. "That's three helpings of onions you've had already. Remember, there's pie for dessert still to come."

"I like onions better than pie—even your pie, Ma," Autie answered.

His father chuckled. "It's a wonder Lydia and her husband could afford to feed you," he said, wiping his bushy beard. "Well, eat while you can, Armstrong. Next fall, when you're a teacher boarding around, you won't find anybody who cooks as well as your mother."

Then he added more seriously, "There's still time to change your mind about teaching, Autie. I can always use you on the farm."

Autie looked up and down the long table. Surely nobody ever had a nicer family. He always missed them a lot when he was away. He missed the gay talk and the whooping, noisy laughter and the jokes they all liked to play on one another.

But as for changing his mind? He shook his head. "If I'm going to be an army officer I'll have to go to West Point," he said. "If I'm going to pass the exams for West Point, I'll have to learn some more mathematics. I can learn it at McNeely Normal School, in Hopedale, evenings. And I need the money from teaching school to pay for the course there. One thing depends on another, you see.

"So I'll just eat hearty and hope for the best," he continued, grinning. "Are there any more onions, Ma?"

The summer passed, and in the fall Autie started his job of teaching in the Beech Point School, at New Athens. He was sunburned and muscular after his work on the farm. Not one of the big tough boys who had bullied other teachers dared to try it on Mr. George Armstrong Custer. The name of Armstrong fitted him too well!

In the evenings Autie studied at the Normal School in Hopedale. Life wasn't all work for him, however. His gaiety and good looks and friendliness made him popular wherever he went. He loved to dance. He could play the accordion well. And whenever a picnic or party was given he was always invited.

Among his new friends was a quiet, pretty girl named Faith. One snowy evening the young people of the village planned a straw ride out to a farmhouse where there was to be a spelling bee. Autie invited Faith to go as his partner.

But Faith's parents were Quakers. They did not believe in war, and they would not allow her to be the partner of a boy who planned to be a soldier. Autie had to watch sadly while another boy named Fred Kingman seated himself beside Faith in the straw-filled sleigh.

He knew that Faith was disappointed, just as he was. When Fred looked at him triumphantly, Autie's temper flared.

"I'm going to get Faith for a partner somehow before this ride is over," he promised himself. Then he climbed up beside his best friend, Joe Dickerson, who was going to drive the horses. "Here, Joe, let me drive for a while," he said.

Joe handed over the reins and off they started. Sleigh bells jingled, and runners squeaked on the hard-packed snow of the village street. The air was crisp and cold. The houses they passed looked like Christmas pictures, with the light from their windows shining golden on the snow.

Soon they were out of the village on a winding country road. In some places the snow had drifted deep across it, making hard pulling for the horses.

When they were halfway through one of these drifts, Autie suddenly jerked the reins to one side. At the same time he flicked the horses with the whip, making them jump forward.

[*40*]

Over went the sleigh, spilling its laughing, screaming load into the soft snowbank. At last the sleigh was finally righted and everybody was aboard again. But Autie Custer, *not* Fred Kingman, was sitting beside Faith!

Fred knew better than to try to get his seat back by force. He waited for his revenge. The boys and girls reached the farmhouse and the spelling bee began.

During the contest, Autie was given a difficult word. While he was trying to spell it, he saw a face pressed against the window across the room. It was Fred Kingman, standing outside in the snow and making horrible grimaces to distract him.

Once again Autie's temper rose quickly. He sprang to his feet and was at the window in one swift leap. He smashed his clenched fist through the pane. It struck Fred squarely on the nose and knocked him backward into the snow.

The sound of breaking glass brought everyone crowding around. "What happened? How did the window get broken?" their hostess cried, hurrying in from the kitchen.

"I did it. I'm sorry. I'll put another windowpane in for you, ma'am," Autie stammered.

"Somebody go out and see if Fred's hurt," she ordered. "Now, young man, let me see your hand."

Autie held up his hand, turning it over in

the lamplight. There was not a mark on it. Nor, by some strange chance, had the glass cut Fred, either. His nose was bleeding from Autie's fist, but there wasn't a scratch on him.

The woman shook her head. "You could have cut an artery and bled to death, right here. And you might have hurt Fred badly, too. It was luck, just plain fool luck, that saved you this time, Armstrong Custer," she said.

CHAPTER V

A Boy on a Black Horse

IT WAS a warm Sunday afternoon in May of 1856. Autie sat at the big dining-room table, writing. His yellow head was bent over his paper. His strong fingers gripped his pen.

"What are you working at so hard, son?" Emmanuel Custer asked.

Autie laid down the pen and leaned back in his chair.

"There, it's finished," he said with a deep sigh. "I've been writing to Mr. Bingham in Washington."

"Mr. Bingham!" exclaimed Autie's mother, who had just entered the room. "Why on earth are you writing to him?"

"Because the only way a boy can get into

West Point is to be appointed by a congress-man," Autie explained, getting to his feet. "And Mr. Bingham's the congressman from our district, so I've written to him and asked him to appoint *me*."

Autie smiled, but his mother did not.

"Autie, I know your heart's been set on being a soldier ever since you were a little boy," she said soberly. "But I've hoped and I've prayed that you would change your mind. Wars and fighting are sinful and wrong, Autie." There were tears in her eyes, and she wiped them off with the edge of her apron.

Autie looked at her sadly, for he loved his mother very much. "I'm sorry, Ma," he answered. "Wars may be wrong, but until men can live in the world without fighting, there are bound to be armies and soldiers."

"But why should *you*, my own son, want so much to be a professional soldier?" asked Mrs. Custer.

For a long moment Autie hesitated. At last he shook his head. "How can a fellow explain the way he's made?" he said. "All I know is that I *do* want it more than anything else in the world."

[*45*]

He sealed the letter and put it into his pocket. "I'll mail this when I get back to Hopedale," he said. Then he kissed his mother warmly and hurried out of the house.

For days, then weeks, Autie waited for the congressman's reply. At last an official-looking letter arrived from Washington. He tore it open, almost too excited to read the words before his eyes.

The letter was courteous and brief. "The appointment to West Point for this year has already been made," it stated. "You will have to apply again next year."

Autie was almost sick with disappointment. "A whole year to wait!" he cried. But it never occurred to him to give up.

"I'd better go back to school and study more math," he decided. "Because I'm going to get to West Point somehow. Even if I have to go to Washington myself to talk to the Honorable Mr. Bingham, I'm going to get that appointment."

It wasn't necessary, however, for Autie to go to Washington. Within a few months the country was in the midst of a hard-fought political campaign. The Democrats had nomi-

nated James Buchanan for President. The
Republicans nominated John C. Fremont.

As Autie left his classroom one afternoon a
friend named Nate Cawley hurried up to him.

"Say, Autie," Nate cried. "Come on with
me. There's going to be a parade, and we can
be in it."

"But that parade's in honor of Fremont,
and he's a Republican," Autie protested.
"Your folks are Democrats, just like mine."

"Shucks, who cares about that?" Nate said.
"They are trying to get a lot of fellows to ride
dressed up as 'Border Ruffians.' You know,
those men who're making all that trouble
along the Kansas-Missouri border. There'll be
horses to ride and free food later. Come on!"

Autie grinned. "Is that right? Sure, then,
I'll come."

The two young fellows hurried off. They
arrived on the run just as the parade was getting started.

"Where are your costumes?" the leader
asked them. "You're supposed to look like
Border Ruffians, not schoolboys."

"That's easy," Autie answered. "We can
smear our faces with dirt and turn our clothes

[47]

inside out. Do you have any horses for us?"

"Well—" the man hesitated. "There are a couple left, over there at the hitching rack, if you want them." He pointed to two rough-coated animals, a black and a brown.

When the boys approached in their make-shift costumes, the black horse sidled away, laying back his ears and rolling his eyes.

"Say, I wouldn't like to ride that black nag. He looks mean," Nate said. "The brown's an old crow-bait, but I choose him."

[48]

"I've never seen a horse *I* couldn't ride," Autie boasted. "I don't think that black nag's mean, though, only scared."

Talking in a low, soothing tone, he approached the nervous horse. He patted him gently until the animal seemed to gain confidence. Then, still talking, he slipped lightly into the saddle.

The horse flung up his head and gave a few sideways jumps. But Autie soon had him under control, and the boys joined the end of the procession.

Crowds lined the streets as they rode along behind the blaring brass band. Republicans cheered the parade. Democrats booed.

Autie's black horse didn't buck any more, but he pranced nervously and was hard to hold in. Just as they were passing the reviewing stand a newspaper blew along the street. The horse was frightened and reared wildly. Autie's skill in quieting his mount brought some applause from the watchers.

"Say, do you know who was up there on the reviewing stand, Autie?" Nate asked, as they rode on again, side by side.

"The mayor, I suppose," Autie answered.

The horse was frightened and reared wildly

"Yes, and somebody else, too. Representative Bingham, the congressman from our district," Nate said.

"Congressman Bingham?" Autie repeated. His heart gave a great leap. "Why, here's my chance!"

The instant they reached the park where the parade ended, he leaped off his horse and tied him quickly to a hitching post.

"I'll see you later, Nate," he called over his shoulder. Then he set off at a run.

Congressman Bingham was just leaving the platform when a quick, excited young voice spoke his name. He turned to see one of the "Border Ruffians" from the parade pushing through the crowd toward him.

"Mr. Bingham, sir. May I speak to you for a minute?" the young man asked him.

The congressman paused good-naturedly. "Of course, of course. You're the fellow who managed his horse so well, aren't you? No mistaking that yellow hair," he said.

"My name's George Armstrong Custer, sir. I wrote to you a few months ago asking for an appointment to West Point. You told me that the place was already filled, but that I could apply again for next year. I really *want* to go to West Point, sir."

"Yes, I remember, now. You wrote a fine letter, my boy," Bingham said, stroking his chin thoughtfully. "Do you think that you'd make a good officer, Custer?"

Autie's bright blue eyes met the older man's steady glance. He straightened his shoulders and stood, erect and tall, before him. "Yes, sir, I *know* I would," he answered.

Congressman Bingham smiled. "I believe you would," he said. "And I'll give you the appointment for next year. But the rest is up to you."

CHAPTER VI

Cadet Custer

O N JUNE 3, 1857, a tall, active young fellow of seventeen stepped off the gangplank of a Hudson River steamer. He looked up with a fast-beating heart at the towering bluffs that rose from the edge of the water.

"I'm really at West Point!" Autie Custer whispered to himself.

The paddlewheels of the steamer thundered away into midstream. Autie shouldered his bag and climbed eagerly upward toward his new life.

The first-year students were called "plebes," young Custer soon learned. He learned also that the upperclassmen, or cadets, hazed the poor plebes from morning until night.

Plebes had to salute the cadets whenever

they met them and had to address them as "sir." Plebes had to obey every command given by a cadet. Plebes were given foolish and ridiculous nicknames, and no matter how much they disliked them, they had to answer to them.

On his first day at the Academy, Custer was stopped by a group of upperclassmen. He was told to stand at attention while they looked him over.

"Well, now, here's a pretty boy," one of the cadets said, grinning. "Look at those sweet pink cheeks and those lovely yellow curls. What shall we call this one, gentlemen?"

"He's even got a dimple in his chin! Fanny's the only name for him," another suggested.

"Fanny Custer! That's your name now, Plebe," the first cadet stated. "Be sure to answer to it promptly."

It was lucky for Custer that he was used to the rough jokes of his brothers. Fanny was a silly name for a strapping six-footer like himself. But it was no worse than the names some of the other plebes had been given.

Late in June all the plebes went into camp on a part of the Academy grounds. They slept in tents on the bare earth and marched and drilled from dawn until dark. Autie didn't mind any of this. The one thing about West Point which really bothered him was the strict discipline. Every moment of every day was planned. He was always under orders which he must obey instantly, without question.

Young Custer could understand the reason for this. The students were learning to be army officers, and an army without discipline wouldn't be an army at all. It would be a weak, unruly mob. But even though he understood this, Autie Custer hated the discipline from the very beginning, and he never got over hating it.

In September the plebes were put into barracks. Four students were assigned to each room. One of Custer's roommates was Jim Parker from Missouri. Next door roomed Tom Rosser, of Texas.

These classmates were both from Southern states. One morning, while they were putting their rooms in order, Custer got into an argument with them. They argued over the bitter quarrel which was growing between the Northern and Southern sections of their country.

It was a quarrel over slavery which had started long before these West Pointers were born. Many years earlier, the people of the Northern states had decided that it was wrong for any man to own another man. They had passed laws against it. But the people in the South still kept slaves.

Meanwhile the country had been growing rapidly. Newly settled lands in the West were being made into states. The Northerners declared that slavery should never be allowed in these new states. The Southerners insisted that they had a right to take their slaves wherever they pleased. This question was discussed again and again in Congress. There were fierce and angry speeches on both sides. Now the Southern states were threatening to leave the Union and set up a government of their own.

"Do you mean that the Southern states will really carry out that threat?" Custer asked Jim Parker and Tom Rosser. He stood with his broom in his hand, looking from one friend to another. "Will they really try to break up the Union?"

"Of course we will, if you Yankees don't stop trying to boss us," Tom Rosser told him.

"But the Federal Government would never allow it," Custer protested.

Jim Parker's eyes flashed. "Let them try to stop us!" he cried. "The thirteen colonies separated from England, didn't they?"

"But, Jim," Custer argued, "it took the Revolutionary War to separate us from England."

"Well—" Parker began. He hesitated, then spoke more soberly. "Maybe it'll come to war

[57]

this time, too. But I hope not. I hope that the North will give in, before it's too late."

Before Custer could answer, the bugle blew, calling them to other duties. There was no more talk that day about the trouble between the North and the South.

Time passed, and a full year went by. Then Plebe Custer became Cadet Custer. But discipline was still hard for him to bear. There were so many rules! It seemed as though he could hardly move without breaking one of them.

West Pointers are always supposed to look smart and trim. Every button must be polished. There must never be a speck of dust on their boots, nor a spot or a crease on their uniforms. Their hair must be cut to a certain length. Their rooms must be in perfect order at all times.

Custer often let his room get untidy, and he was careless in his dress. He sometimes forgot to have his hair cut until it was far too long. Then he cut it himself with horse clippers from the cavalry stable!

At the end of each term there were many black marks against his name on the record books because of rules which he had broken. He knew that if he received too many black marks he would be dismissed from the Academy. But somehow he managed to keep that from happening.

"So you're still here among us, Fanny?" Jim Parker said, grinning, when Custer's fourth year began. "How did you ever scrape through? I thought you were sunk last term for sure."

"Let's call it 'Custer Luck,'" Tom Rosser said. "You can squeeze through here at the Point where the officers know you and like you, Fanny. But wait until you're out and in the army. Promotions come hard, there. You'll still be a second lieutenant when you're fifty!"

"Maybe I'll be lucky there, too," Custer laughed. "Wait and see. I'll bet I'm a general before any of you."

A shadow crossed Jim Parker's face. "If there's a war, promotions will come fast for us all," he said. "But we won't be in the same armies."

There was a silence then. War between the states seemed almost certain now. West Point was divided sharply between the Northern and Southern boys. In November, 1860, Abraham Lincoln, who hated slavery, was elected President. When news of this reached West Point, two of the Southern cadets resigned at once and went home. And then, in December, the state of South Carolina left the Union.

One February afternoon Custer was dismounting at the stables after field artillery practice. He had been riding Wellington, his favorite of all the horses in the troop.

"Say good-by to that horse, Mr. Custer,"

Trooper McCarthy told him as he unsaddled. "We've got orders to take this battery of artillery to Washington. They're afraid that there'll be riots in the city when President Lincoln is inaugurated there next month. They've called in soldiers to keep order."

Custer gave Wellington an affectionate pat as he left him. "Good-by, old fellow," he said. "You're a good horse. I'd like to ride you again."

There was no trouble in Washington when Lincoln was inaugurated in March. But by that time six more Southern states had left the Union. They had formed their own government which they called the Confederate States of America. And on April twelfth came news which shook the whole country.

Fort Sumter, which belonged to the Government of the United States, had been attacked by Southern soldiers.

"They've shot our soldiers! The Rebels have fired on the Stars and Stripes! It's war!" newsboys shouted all through the North.

President Lincoln called at once for soldiers to join the Northern Army. "The Union must and shall be preserved!" he stated. He was determined to bring the Southern states back into the Union, even by force, if necessary.

˒ The West Point class which was to graduate in June was hurried out in April, instead, and it was sent off to join the army. Custer's class was told to prepare for graduation in June.

"That means we get out with only four years training instead of five," thought Custer.

The weeks passed quickly. On the day before graduation Custer was serving on guard duty in camp on the Academy grounds. As he paced around the corner of a tent he came upon two cadets who were arguing violently. Suddenly one cadet struck the other. In an instant they were whaling each other with their fists.

Some friends of one of the fighters came running up to join the fray.

"Wait a minute! Stand back, boys. Let's have a fair fight," Custer told them.

Quickly a ring was formed and the two angry cadets squared off while the other students waited eagerly.

"They're evenly matched. This is going to be a fight worth watching," Custer exclaimed.

[*62*]

No one noticed that the officer of the day had arrived on the scene, until his voice rang out harshly. "Who's on guard duty here?" he demanded.

Custer came stiffly to attention. Too late, he remembered that guards were supposed to stop all fights, not to encourage them!

"You are under arrest. Go to your tent and stay there!" the officer told him.

Next day, while his classmates graduated and received their commissions as army officers, Custer sat staring dismally at the canvas wall of his tent.

"Is this going to be the end of everything I've planned and hoped for?" he asked himself. "Will I be sent home, disgraced forever? No, I won't believe that. I *belong* in the army! There's a war starting, and I've *got* to fight in it! This just can't happen now—not to me!"

CHAPTER VII

Custer's First Battle

THERE was wild confusion in the city of
Washington. The streets were swirling rivers
of dust. Everywhere soldiers were marching
and dispatch riders were galloping here and
there.

"The Rebel Army is gathered in Virginia.
They'll attack our city at any moment," a man
shouted across the crowd to a friend.

"Don't worry. General McDowell will stop
them. He'll soon have them on the run," came
the reply.

Through the excited throngs crowding the
streets, Second Lieutenant George Armstrong
Custer pushed his way toward the Adjutant
General's office. Again he had been lucky. He
had only been kept under arrest at West Point

for two weeks. Then he had been released and given his commission as second lieutenant. Now he was hurrying to the Adjutant General's office to report for duty.

On the way to Washington he had stopped in New York to buy a fine new uniform. A shining sabre hung in its sheath at his side. Spurs jingled on the heels of his cavalry boots. He knew that he needed a haircut, as usual, but there was no time for that now.

He was only worried about one thing. "What if the war ends before I can get to the fighting?" he thought.

When he reached the Adjutant General's office it, too, was crowded. He had to wait until two o'clock in the morning before it was his turn to report.

While he was being given his orders, General Winfield Scott, Commander in Chief, came through the office. The stout old general was attracted by the bright, eager look of the young officer. He paused to speak to him.

"I'll give you your choice," he said. "Do you want to drill troops here in Washington, or do you wish to join the Second Cavalry at the front?"

"I'll go to the front," Custer answered instantly.

Scott smiled. "Good!" he said. "Report back here with a mount this evening. I'll have some dispatches ready for you to take to General McDowell in Centerville."

As soon as it was daylight, Custer set out on a search for a horse. He tramped the streets from one livery stable to another, but always the answer was the same. "A horse? Today? You might as well ask for an elephant, Lieutenant. All the horses in Washington have been taken by the cavalry troops. There just aren't any left."

But Custer did not give up his search. Late in the afternoon he heard a voice shout his name from the crowded street. Trooper McCarthy, who had been at West Point, was riding toward him. He was leading a second horse, and it was Wellington!

"How are you, Lieutenant?" McCarthy called. "I'm glad to see you got your commission after all."

Custer sprang to his side. "Where are you going with that horse?" he demanded.

"Out to Centerville, to Colonel Griffin."

"I've orders to report there, too, to General McDowell, and I've got to have a mount. Let me ride him," Custer begged.

The trooper hesitated. But when Custer explained that he was to carry dispatches from General Scott himself, McCarthy handed over the reins promptly.

"We'll make better time anyway, if you ride him than if I lead him," he said. "I guess that luck the boys talked about is still with you, Lieutenant Custer."

Custer picked up the dispatches at General Scott's headquarters. Then the two riders set off toward the front. They rode rapidly all through the summer night. About three o'clock in the morning they reached General McDowell's headquarters at Centerville, Virginia.

Custer dismounted. He gave Wellington a farewell pat. Then he handed his reins to the trooper.

"Thanks for the ride, McCarthy, and good luck to you," he said.

McCarthy saluted. "Good-by, Lieutenant. And may *your* good luck hold out, sir," he answered.

Custer returned his salute. Then he hurried to complete his mission. He gave General Scott's dispatches to a worried-looking major who was General McDowell's aide.

"Where can I find the Second Cavalry, sir? I'm to report to Lieutenant Drummond, Troop G, for duty," Custer asked him.

"Good heavens! How should I know?" the aide snapped. "Somewhere off in that direction," and he waved his hand vaguely.

Custer set off on foot through the dark, sleeping camp that stretched for miles over the countryside. Whenever he met a sentry pacing his beat he asked directions. He found the 2nd Cavalry at dawn just as the bugles roused the men from where they lay rolled in their blankets. Near by, in an open pasture, the cavalry horses dozed or moved restlessly, tied in long picket lines.

"You're just in time for breakfast," Lieutenant Drummond said, when Custer introduced himself. "Better eat it right away, because we'll be mounting within the hour."

The soldiers were eating from tin plates around an open campfire. Custer hungrily ate the beefsteak and corn bread which the cook handed him. As he gulped the last of his coffee the bugles sounded the order for "Boots and saddles."

"Here's a horse for you," Drummond told him. "We're really going into action this time."

They mounted and rode to the head of the line.

"The Rebels are at Manassas, along a stream called Bull Run," Drummond explained, as they jogged along. "Manassas is an important railway junction. We want to take it away from the Rebs. Our particular job is to protect Colonel Griffin's men while they get their cannon into place. They're moving along parallel with us, just over that ridge."

The sun grew hotter as the hours passed. Dust raised by the trotting horses boiled up around them in choking clouds. Custer's new uniform was no longer blue, but gray with dust and streaked with sweat.

At last an orderly came galloping up with a message. "The battery of cannon is in position. You are to halt and wait here on this slope for further orders," he said.

Suddenly the crack and thunder of firing came to them clearly. The battle had begun! A strange, pricking sensation ran up Custer's spine. His heart beat fast.

"This is my first battle," he thought. "What will it be like? Will we make a charge?"

Another question rose in his mind. "Which weapon am I supposed to use first in a charge, my sabre or my pistol?" He drew out his sabre. Then he changed his mind and took out his pistol instead. "No, I guess the sabre was right, after all," he decided.

Then he noticed that a young officer near

him was copying his movements. When he met Custer's glance, the officer flushed.

"I'm new at this," he confessed. "This is my first day in the army as a volunteer. So I thought I'd be safe if I copied a West Pointer like you."

Custer threw back his head and laughed. "I'm pretty new myself," he answered. "We'll let Drummond tell us which weapons to use when he gives the command to charge."

They waited for hours, but there was no command to charge. The noise of firing began to come from another direction and it grew fainter. Still the cavalrymen waited. Their horses stamped and shifted impatiently in the hot sun.

At four o'clock in the afternoon, Lieutenant Drummond dismounted. "Custer, I want to see what's going on," he said. "Come along."

The two men climbed the hillside. From its crest they could see Colonel Griffin's battery of cannon lined up on another slope across a little valley. A long file of infantry soldiers was moving along the valley floor and passing the edge of a thick wood beyond.

"Well, our men are still advancing. I wonder where the Rebels are. They aren't putting up much of a battle, after all," Drummond said.

"Our side seems to be winning, sir, even if we haven't had our own chance to fight," Custer remarked.

He longed to be where the bullets flew thickest. Enviously he watched the blue-clad soldiers filing below.

"Here come some more men out of the woods, sir," he said. "But look!" he shouted suddenly. "That's not *our* flag. Those men are

[*73*]

Rebels! They've taken our men by surprise! They're attacking on the flank!"

The snap and rattle of rifle fire came up to the two watchers.

"Why doesn't Griffin's battery shoot at the Rebs?" Drummond cried. "They could blow them all sky high!"

But even as he spoke, it was too late. With a crashing roar, shells began to burst among Griffin's cannon, hiding them in smoke and dust. The battery, too, had been surprised by Confederate artillerymen who were hidden in the woods.

Before Custer's horrified eyes the Union troops broke and ran. They were untried soldiers who had never been under shellfire before. They dropped their weapons and fled.

Drummond and Custer hurried back to their own men.

"Now we'll be ordered to charge. We'll counterattack," Custer told himself. "If we counterattack at once, those frightened infantrymen will have a chance to rally."

But the order to charge never came. Instead, came an order for the 2nd Cavalry to join the retreat! Fiercely angry though he was, Custer had to obey. The whole Union Army was flee-ing in panic toward Washington. He saw many of his own men in Troop G give way to terror under the screaming shells. Soldiers and horses were killed all around him. But he himself felt no fear at all, only bitter disappointment.

"We're being beaten," he thought angrily, "and I haven't had a single chance to fight!" He stared back into the flame and smoke that hid the Confederate cannon. "If only I could get one crack at them!" he almost prayed, gripping the hilt of his sabre.

But the cavalry was ordered to fall back again toward Washington. The road was strewn now with the weapons, packs, and equipment dropped by the fleeing soldiers.

A downpour of rain began at sunset. Troop G splashed on through the mud all night long. By morning they had reached the Potomac River across from Washington. There Mc-Dowell halted his army at last.

"You're a cool-headed youngster under fire," Lieutenant Drummond said to Custer, as they dismounted stiffly. "I'm going to give you credit for that in my report."

[75]

CHAPTER VIII

A Taste of Glory

IT'S good to have you home again, Armstrong," Emmanuel Custer said affectionately, as he laid down his fork. "We were worried when we heard you were ill."

"It's good to be here, Pa," his son answered. "And I'm glad you've all moved here to Monroe, near Lydia. Now I can see everyone whenever I come home on leave."

The whole family was gathered round the big dining table. It was almost like being back on the farm, Custer thought, looking at the circle of faces. The house was different, of course, but the table and people were the same. And so was the cooking!

"Got any more onions, Ma?" he asked.

"Of course. Help yourself, Autie," his mother said, smiling. "You're feeling better now, aren't you?"

"Yes, I feel fine," Autie answered. "Chills and fever can lay a man low, but they don't last forever."

Tom leaned forward in his chair. "Tell us more about the war, Autie," he urged. "After Bull Run, what did you do?"

"Hung around Washington waiting for orders," Autie told him. "Then I came down with chills and fever and they gave me sick leave and sent me home to get well."

"What will happen when you get back?" Margaret asked, passing Autie some hot biscuits. "Will you stay in the cavalry?"

"Of course," her brother assured her. "President Lincoln has organized a new army called the Army of the Potomac, and he's put General McClellan in command. I hope we'll get a chance soon to pay back the Rebels for the licking we took at Bull Run."

Custer's sick leave lasted for three months. Then he went back to his regiment which was now called the 5th Cavalry. Soon he heard good news. General McClellan was planning to attack Manassas Junction near Bull Run. He wanted to gain control of the railroads there. In February, the general ordered the Army of the Potomac to advance into Virginia.

One morning a section of the 5th Cavalry halted to rest their horses at the foot of a hill near Catlett's Station. Suddenly a messenger came spurring toward them. He pulled up his horse before a lean, yellow-haired officer.

"Where's your company commander?" he demanded.

"The captain and first lieutenant just went to the rear—they were called back for a conference," the young officer answered. "I'm Second Lieutenant Custer. I guess I'm in charge for the time being."

"This message is for you then, sir," the courier said. "Confederate pickets are holding that hill above the railroad. You are ordered to charge and take it from them."

Custer's heart gave a wild leap. "Our first charge, and *I'm* to lead it!" he thought.

He saw the top sergeant and a corporal exchange worried glances. He could almost read their minds. "Can *that* youngster lead a charge?" they seemed to be thinking.

[78]

"I'll have to show them that I know my business," Custer told himself. Swiftly he gave his orders. The bugler blew the shrill, stirring notes of command, and the troopers formed their line, ready to advance. Custer rose high in his stirrups. He waved his sword above his head in a glittering arc.

"Charge!" he yelled at the top of his lungs. "Come on, boys! Charge! Follow me!"

Spurring his horse, he dashed up the hill at a headlong gallop. He did not look back, but he could hear the thunder of drumming hoofs behind him. His men were there, riding close at his heels.

Puffs of smoke showed suddenly on the hilltop and bullets whistled in the air past Custer's head. He heard a hoarse cry. A man was down! But there was no stopping now.

"Come on, boys!" he shouted again.

The Confederates stood their ground. But only for a moment. The onrushing cavalry and its wildly whooping, sabre-swinging leader were too much for them. They fled down the other side of the hill and across a bridge. Then they set fire to the bridge so that their pursuers could not follow them.

With the enemy routed, the cavalry took possession of the hilltop. Custer turned to his sergeant. "What man was hit?" he asked.

"Trooper Bryaut, sir," the sergeant answered. "A bullet creased his scalp, but I think he'll be all right."

Leaving the sergeant in charge on the hill, Custer rode back. He dismounted beside the wounded man, who lay on the ground.

"How do you feel, Bryaut?" he asked, bending over him. "Here comes the surgeon now. He'll soon have you fixed up. You're going to be famous, you know. You've shed the first blood in the Army of the Potomac!"

"I feel all right now, Lieutenant," Bryaut replied, with a plucky grin. "And I'm ready to follow you anywhere else you lead us, sir."

Custer mounted and rode on to regimental headquarters to make his report. "I've led a cavalry charge at last!" he thought. His heart was still pounding with excitement. He had had a taste of glory, and he longed for more.

For several weeks, however, his regiment did no more fighting. Custer was impatient and eager for action. Day after day, he hung around headquarters, hoping to be sent on a difficult or dangerous mission.

His captain called to him from his tent one morning. "Custer! The engineers have asked for an observation officer. Want to volunteer?"

"Yes, sir!" Custer answered eagerly. Then he learned that the observing was to be done from a great, gas-filled balloon. Custer was seldom afraid, but he felt a little uneasy when he saw the huge ball bobbing and leaping about in the wind like an animal on a leash!

A flimsy-looking basket hung from the balloon. As Custer and the balloonist climbed into it, it creaked under their weight. The balloon began to rise rapidly into the air.

"Will this thing really hold us both?" Custer asked.

For answer the balloonist jumped up and down as hard as he could. "See, it's good and strong," he said.

Custer gripped the sides of the basket and hoped with all his heart that the man was right. But when they were aloft, a thousand feet above the earth, he began to enjoy the strange sensation. The landscape spread out below them as though it were drawn on an enormous, colored map—of enemy positions!

"Why, this is wonderful!" Custer exclaimed. "If only we could find some way to propel the balloon and steer it, we might change the whole art of war!"

"Things like that will be done some day," the balloonist assured him.

"Why, this is wonderful!" Custer exclaimed

Custer took careful observations and reported them to headquarters when they reached the earth again. He went up in the balloon every day, and often at night, for some weeks after that.

Then he was recalled to his regiment. Soon McClellan ordered his army to advance farther into Virginia. The main part of the Rebel army held a strong position just south of the Chickahominy River. There were no bridges across the river and General Barnard, the chief of the engineers, decided that he must find a shallow place where the Union forces could cross.

"Come along, Lieutenant," he said to Autie Custer, who happened to be near him. "I may need you."

The two men made their way cautiously through a swamp to the bank of the river. "I wonder how deep it is," Barnard said.

"I'll find out, General Barnard," Custer answered quickly. He unbuckled his pistol. Holding it high, he jumped into the dark, sluggish water. In the deepest part the stream came only up to his armpits. "It's fordable, sir," he reported. Then he went on.

He knew that the Rebel forces were somewhere on the other side and he wanted to have
a look at them. Climbing out on the opposite
bank, he crept silently forward to where a
thicket blocked his view. He peered cautiously
through the trees and saw that Confederate
soldiers were encamped along the stream.

"There are about a hundred men there,"
he calculated quickly. "And they've put themselves in a bend of the river where we could
cut them off and capture them easily."

He slid back into the water, waded quietly
across, and told his news to Barnard.

"This may interest General McClellan," said General Barnard. "Come with me."

At McClellan's headquarters, Barnard gave his report, while the muddy, bedraggled young lieutenant stood dripping behind him. McClellan was interested. He asked Custer several questions about what he had seen.

At the end of the interview he looked at Custer thoughtfully. "I can use a man who can make a clear report of what he sees under dangerous conditions," he said. "Would you care to be one of my aides? I can offer you the rank of captain."

Custer was almost too surprised to answer. But he managed to stammer out, "Yes—yes, sir. Yes, of course, General, if you really *mean* it!"

He returned to his tent with his head whirling. His boots were heavy with the water that sloshed at every step he took, but he felt as though he were walking on air.

"So I'm an aide to the commander in chief, and promoted to captain," he thought. "Maybe the 'Custer Luck' that the boys at West Point used to joke about is real, after all."

CHAPTER IX

The Young General

BOSTON CUSTER stood waiting on the railway station platform in Monroe, Michigan. He stamped his feet and swung his arms, for the winter air was cold. From far down the track came a faint, distant whistle. The train was coming and his soldier brother, Autie, would be on it!

The train roared in and pulled to a stop with a great clanging of bells and hissing of steam. And there was Autie in his blue uniform leaping down the steps, the first man off the train.

"Bos!" cried Autie, folding his young brother in his arms in a great bear hug. "My, but you've grown! How is everybody at home?"

"We're all fine," Boston answered. He picked up Autie's bag and the two started along the snowy street. "Well, how does it feel to be a captain, Autie?"

Autie's smile faded and he looked suddenly grim. "I'm not a captain any more, Bos. I'm only a first lieutenant," he answered.

"But—but what happened?" Boston asked, his eyes round.

"General McClellan isn't in command of the Army of the Potomac any more, that's what happened," Autie said indignantly. "He's the best general in the country, I think. But even *he* couldn't do miracles. Anyway, he didn't win victories fast enough, so now he's fired. And I was on his staff, so of course I was demoted too. They gave me this leave of absence to wait for another assignment. That's why I was able to get home."

"Well," said Boston, drawing a long breath. "Well, that doesn't seem fair to *me*. But I'm glad you're here, anyway. Because Tom's gone off to join the army and Ma's awful upset."

"Tom in the army!" Autie exclaimed. "Well, good for Tom! But I'm sorry for Ma," he added hastily. He quickened his stride

[*88*]

down the icy street with Boston trotting beside him.

It was wonderful to be with his family again. And Autie Custer enjoyed seeing his friends. Monroe was a gay place that season. The pretty girls gave parties for soldiers who were home on leave during the winter months when there was no fighting.

At one of the parties Custer found himself dancing in a quadrille opposite a slim, graceful girl. She was dressed in white and a red rose was pinned in her hair. Her dark eyes smiled up into his blue ones as they moved forward and back in the steps of the quadrille.

It was Libbie Bacon. Autie wanted desperately to speak to her. But all at once his mouth felt dry and he could not say a word.

Libbie spoke to him first. "Hello, you Custer boy!" she said mischievously, just as she had, years before, at her own front gate.

Then the pattern of the dance drew them apart. She whirled away in the arms of her partner. But through the rest of the quadrille Autie's eyes followed her about the room. Before the party was over he had asked her if he might call on her.

After that Custer went several times to Libbie's home. Soon he knew that he was deeply in love. But when he asked Libbie's father if he might marry Libbie, Judge Bacon refused.

"I do not wish Elizabeth to marry a lieutenant who has no money but his pay," he stated. "Please discontinue your visits."

Custer could not persuade Libbie to marry him against her father's wishes. "We'll have to wait, Armstrong," she said. "I'm sure that in time Father will change his mind."

Sadly disappointed, Autie Custer went back to duty with his old regiment, the 5th Cavalry.

Early in June the cavalrymen were riding on a scouting mission near the Blue Ridge Mountains. Suddenly an attacking force of Confederate cavalry dashed out upon them from some woods. The Union troopers fought back and seemed to be winning, when more Southern horsemen joined the battle. J. E. B. Stuart, smartest of all Rebel cavalry leaders, was leading them.

Sabre clanged against sabre as men shouted wildly and horses reared. Pistols cracked. Dust and smoke rose up in clouds.

The Union general's horse was killed under

him and he fell to the ground. The Union colonel was shot dead just as he tried to rally his troopers for a countercharge. The Union cavalry began to fall back.

Then suddenly, above the noise and the gun smoke, came a shout like a bugle call.

"Come on, boys! Come on, let's get 'em this time!" It was young Custer, swinging his sabre and riding straight toward Stuart's men. "Come on, boys!" he shouted again.

With an answering roar his men spurred forward to follow the yellow hair that shone through the dust like a bright flag. There was another desperate, hand-to-hand struggle and this time the Union men were victorious. They captured a hundred prisoners and a Rebel banner.

"It's 'Custer Luck'!" a trooper said to his comrade as they unsaddled that evening in camp. "It's a wonder the lieutenant wasn't killed! Did you see him ride out by himself after the Rebs? When I saw him go I thought to myself, 'Good-by, old Curly!' But look at him now. Grinning and fresh as a daisy. Not a scratch on him! There's nobody can match him."

The story of Custer's fight with Jeb Stuart's famous riders spread through the whole Union Army. The Northern forces had won few victories lately, and this was welcome news.

"You should get a promotion out of that fight," Custer's friend, Lieutenant George Yates, told him.

"I'd sure like to be a captain again," Custer

said. "But after all, I'm only twenty-three. I guess I'm lucky to be a first lieutenant."

"You used to say you'd be a general before the war was over," Yates reminded him.

Custer grinned. "Well, maybe I will, George, if it lasts long enough," he answered.

[93]

On June 27th Custer returned to his tent in camp to find Yates waiting for him. There was an excited gleam in George's eyes.

"Good evening, General Custer," he said.

Another officer stepped up and saluted smartly.

"Congratulations, General," he added.

Custer stared at them both. "All right. What's the joke?" he demanded.

"Look inside your tent, Armstrong," Yates said.

On the camp table beside Custer's cot lay an envelope. It was an official army envelope —addressed to Brigadier General George Armstrong Custer.

The young lieutenant's knees gave way under him and he sat down heavily on his camp stool. He picked up the envelope with shaking hands. Inside it was his commission as a Brigadier General of Volunteers in the United States Army!

Still he could not believe it. "But—but what does this mean?" he stammered.

"Just what it says," Yates assured him. "Farnsworth and Merritt have been made brigadier generals, too. The army needs more cavalry fast and of course there have to be officers to lead it."

"And you new generals will have to show now that you are worth your stars," Yates

added. "A dispatch rider has just come in with news. The Confederates are marching into Pennsylvania. General Lee is commanding them. He's aiming at Philadelphia, or New York, and we've got to stop him."

CHAPTER X

Gettysburg, and After

Brigadier general custer was dressing carefully in his tent in the army camp at Hanover, Pennsylvania. In a few moments he was to take command of his brigade. The young general fastened the last button of his jacket and spoke to George Yates, who sat on the edge of a cot, reading a letter.

"Well, George, how do you like my new uniform?" he asked.

Yates looked up and gave a long whistle. "Whew!" he said. "It's certainly a change from that old cavalry jacket of yours. But it isn't strictly regulation, is it?"

Custer grinned. "A general doesn't have to wear the regular uniform, George. When I learned that, I decided to please myself."

"It's a fancy outfit," Yates chuckled. "There's no doubt about that." He looked his friend over from head to foot.

Custer's jacket and trousers were of black velveteen. Wide loops of gold braid adorned his sleeves. Gold stars were embroidered on the collar tabs of his dark blue shirt. His flowing neckerchief was of brilliant scarlet silk.

Now, still grinning, Custer buckled on his sabre. He set his hat at a rakish angle, and gave a twist to the ends of his yellow mustache.

"Well, I guess we'd better go, George," he said, and strode out, with spurs jingling, to his waiting horse.

The men of the brigade were mounted and lined up, ready to be inspected by their new commander. They stared in amazement as he rode along their ranks on his prancing thoroughbred.

"A boy general with curly golden hair!" a veteran trooper muttered scornfully. "A dressed-up dandy!"

"I've heard he's quite a fighter," his comrade reminded him. "Anyway, he sure knows how to ride that horse!"

Two days later Custer and his brigade were at Gettysburg in the midst of the greatest battle of the whole Civil War. And his soldiers learned there that the "boy general with golden hair" was a superb leader of cavalry.

For three days the armies of the North and South fought desperately. Custer charged again and again at the head of his troops. He smashed his way through the enemy lines, yelling and swinging his sabre, and his men followed wherever he led them. Hundreds were killed and wounded all around him. But neither sword nor bullet nor shell touched Custer himself.

"It's Custer Luck! The Rebs just can't kill old Curly!" his men said to each other.

At last the great battle was over. The Northern troops had held fast, and Lee was forced to turn his defeated army back toward Virginia. But many thousands of men from both sides lay dead on that battlefield. There was scarcely a village or town in the whole country which did not mourn for men killed at Gettysburg.

Both armies had to take time, then, to fill up their ranks with fresh soldiers before they could fight again.

Custer used these weeks to drill and train his brigade in their camp in Amosville, Virginia.

"I'm going to have the best cavalry outfit in the army," he told George Yates, as they sat in the shade of his tent one August afternoon. He turned as an officer stepped up and saluted.

"General," said the officer, "do you remember that group of colored people who escaped into our lines this morning? There's a woman among them who is asking to talk with you."

"Send her along, Captain Lyon," Custer ordered.

Lyon left. When he returned, a middle-aged

[*99*]

colored woman in a neat cotton dress was with him.

"Do you wish to speak to me?" Custer asked.

The woman looked at him doubtfully. "You look too young to be a general," she said.

"I'm the general, all right," Custer answered, smiling. "Now what can I do for you?"

"Well—" she hesitated. "That's just what I was going to ask *you*, General. You see, I used to be a slave. When I heard that Mr. Lincoln had sent you Yankees to free us folks, I decided I wouldn't just set down and wait to be freed. I'd help to free myself. So I left my master and came along. And now I want to know what I can do to help."

Custer looked into the earnest dark face. "You mean you'd like to help us win the war?" he asked.

"Yes, sir," she nodded. "That's what I came for. My name's Eliza and I'm a real good cook, General."

"How would you like to cook for me?"

Now it was Eliza's turn to study the blue eyes in the sunburned face before her.

"I'd like that fine, General," she said.

So the bargain was made. Custer found an old carriage for Eliza and gave her two horses to pull it. She loaded it with her supplies and cooking pots. Driving it herself, she followed Custer throughout the rest of the war.

When September came, Custer and his brigade went into action again. They were ordered to attack and capture a railway station at Culpeper, Virginia.

They halted for a rest near the town. Custer called his officers to him for final orders. He spread out his map.

"There are three enemy batteries hidden somewhere here," he said, pointing with his finger. "Our cavalry will advance along this creek bed, which will hide our approach. As soon as our own guns have silenced the Rebel batteries, we'll charge in and take the town."

The blue-clad soldiers rode cautiously forward, hidden by the trees along the creek. But soon the stream spread out into a marshy swamp. Many of the horses sank fetlock deep into the mud, slowing the whole brigade.

Custer rode ahead with a small group of men. As they neared the town, he saw an engine with a train of cars standing at the station.

"That's a Confederate supply train," he told his troopers, "and the engine's getting up steam. We can't let it escape. We've got to capture it."

Suddenly there was a burst of cannon fire. Custer dashed forward. "Go for the locomotive! Capture the train crew!" he shouted.

Then a shell struck near by with a crashing roar. Custer felt a blow on his leg. At that same instant his horse stumbled and fell dead under him. Custer struggled to his feet. One leg felt numb. But, worst of all, he could see the supply train rumbling away.

Captain Lyon galloped up with a spare horse. "At least we made the Rebs show where they are," Custer said grimly as he climbed into the saddle. "Listen! Our own guns are getting them!"

He marshaled his men back out of range of the shells. Then, when the artillery had finished its work, the cavalry swept the remaining Rebels out of the town and captured it.

Custer's leg felt painfully stiff when he dismounted at last. The inside of his boot was wet with blood.

"Is anything wrong, General?" Captain Lyon asked anxiously.

"Yes, I've lost a good horse," Custer said. "And I guess the shell that killed him nicked me, too."

There was a flesh wound in Custer's thigh. After the surgeon had treated it, Autie was given twenty days sick leave. He traveled back to Monroe—and Libbie.

"Father has changed his mind, Armstrong," Libbie told him happily, when they met. "He boasts to everyone, now, that the famous General Custer is a friend of ours."

Soon Custer had Libbie's promise to marry him on his next leave. On February 8, 1864, they were married. But honeymoons are short in wartime. Within two weeks he was at the front again. The war, which had already destroyed so many homes and farms and towns and brave young lives, still dragged on.

CHAPTER XI

A Present for Libbie

Iᴛ WAS the morning of April 9, 1865. Horsemen of Custer's division were lined up under a grove of oak trees on a hillside near Appomattox Court House, Virginia.

All the day before, they had skirmished against Lee's fast-moving Army of Northern Virginia. And then, all night, they had ridden hard through the darkness around the Rebel Army, to cut across the Lynchburg road ahead of it.

Now the men were hollow-eyed from lack of sleep. But they were too excited to feel weary, as they waited for the enemy to appear along the road across the valley.

"We've *got* to stop them!" Custer told his

brother Tom. "We've got to hold them here until our infantry and big guns arrive. If Lee breaks through our line and gets to Lynchburg, he'll find supplies and fresh troops. If we can hold him, it may be the end of the war!"

Tom nodded. He had become a well-trained cavalryman, and had fought bravely at his brother's side in many battles. As he looked at Autie now, sitting in his saddle as straight and keen as a sword blade, he thought of the year that had just passed.

So much had happened in that year! So many skirmishes and battles—Tom couldn't even remember all of their names. President Lincoln had appointed a new commander in chief—General Ulysses S. Grant. Grant had won victories against the Rebels in the west, and now he was pounding out victories here in Virginia.

He had put General Sheridan in command of the cavalry. And Sheridan had made good use of Autie's skill and daring. He had given Autie command of a whole division. He had even recommended that Autie be promoted as soon as possible to the rank of major general.

"Major general, at twenty-five!" Tom thought. "Autie will be the youngest major general in the army. The youngest this country has *ever* had, since Lafayette!"

He turned at the sound of hoofbeats behind them. A courier dashed up and stopped before Autie.

"General!" he reported, saluting. "Our infantry's in sight. They'll be in place and ready for action within half an hour."

"Fine!" Custer exclaimed. "They made good time."

"But look! Here come the Rebels now!" Tom cried.

Dust was beginning to rise where the Lynchburg road emerged from some trees across the valley. Soon a ragged column of men in gray came slowly into sight. They seemed to hesitate. Then they stopped, looking back into the woods.

"What are they going to do?" Tom asked.

"Better not wait to see," Custer said. "Bugler, prepare to sound the charge!" He drew out his sabre and gathered up his reins.

But before he could shout another command, a single rider rode briskly toward them

[*107*]

from the enemy lines. Tom could see that he was carrying something which fluttered above his head. Soon it was clearly visible—a towel tied to a stick. A white flag! *A flag of truce!*

"Where in either army could anyone find a

towel, and one so white?" Tom found himself wondering.

But Custer had already sheathed his sword. He spurred toward the oncoming rider and saluted when they met.

The gray-clad officer returned his salute. His face was pale, but he spoke in a clear, steady voice.

"Sir," he said, "General Lee desires that both armies stop fighting until he can hear from General Grant as to the proposed surrender."

Surrender! A feeling like a shock swept over Custer. The news was almost too great to believe. Then he recovered himself.

"Come with me, sir," he said courteously. "I'll send your message at once to General Sheridan."

Soon Custer, with Sheridan and his staff, were riding swiftly up the long hill to Appomattox Court House. A number of horses and a group of men in blue uniforms were standing in front of an oblong brick house. One of the Union officers stepped forward and saluted as Sheridan dismounted.

"General Lee is already here, in this house,

[*109*]

sir," he announced. "And here is General Grant just arriving."

Sheridan saluted the slight, bearded commander in chief in the dusty blue uniform. Together they mounted the steps and entered the house. Sheridan's aides and Custer joined the other officers who waited outside.

It was warm and bright in the spring sunshine and a soft breeze brought the scent of blossoming orchards. The waiting men moved quietly and spoke softly, almost in whispers, as though they were in church. Everyone felt that this was a great and important meeting.

At last, about four o'clock in the afternoon, the door opened and the two great leaders of the North and South emerged. Lee mounted his gray horse, Traveller, and rode away, tall and handsome in the afternoon light, with his aides behind him. Grant and all the Union officers stood bareheaded until Lee had gone.

General Lee had surrendered. The war was over!

Thousands of men had been killed, homes and farms, villages and towns, even cities had been burned and destroyed. Families all through the land had lost fathers, brothers,

[*110*]

sons, and husbands. But the Union had been saved and the slaves were free!

Custer and his division were ordered back to camp near Petersburg. As soon as Custer reached there, he sent for Libbie, and she came, breathless with happiness.

"The war is over, and *you* are safe!" she cried.

"I have a present for you," Custer told her. "It's from General Sheridan. But first, here's a letter he sent you."

Libbie read the letter aloud:

"My dear Madam,

Permit me to present to you the table upon which were signed the terms of surrender of the Army of Northern Virginia, under General Robert E. Lee; and in conclusion let me add that I know of no person more instrumental in bringing about this most desirable event than your most gallant husband.

I am, Madam, most truly your friend
Philip H. Sheridan, Mj. Gen., U. S. A."

There were tears on Libbie's cheeks as she folded the letter. "I shall keep this forever," she said. "And the table too, of course. But I

[*111*]

couldn't possibly be prouder of you, Autie, than I am already."

A few weeks later the cavalry was lined up, ready to march. Custer and his Libbie rode to the head of the long column of mounted men. Both were superb riders, and both had beautiful horses.

"Three cheers for old Curly!" the troopers shouted as the two took their places.

"And three more for his pretty missus!" another yelled. The cheers thundered to the sky. Then, with Custer and his wife leading, the cavalry started toward Washington.

"There's going to be the biggest parade in history as soon as all the armies can be marched back to the Capital," Custer said. "If only we could see old Abe Lincoln smiling down at us as we ride by!"

His face grew sad at the thought of Lincoln. Throughout the country there was rejoicing because peace had come at last. But there was great grief too, in the hearts of many. For Abraham Lincoln had been shot down by an assassin only five days after Lee's surrender.

The armies paraded late in May through the streets of the Capital. Bands played, crowds

[*112*]

He watched proudly while his son rode past

cheered, and pretty girls threw flowers. But the soldiers marched in review before another President. No tall, stooping figure, no familiar, rugged, beloved face was there to greet them.

Emmanuel Custer journeyed to Washington to watch proudly while his son rode past in the grand review. "You'll be given leave now to come home, won't you, Armstrong?" he asked, when it was over.

Custer shook his head. "I'm sorry, Pa. But I'm still in the army, and I've been ordered to an army post out in Texas. I'll have to start tomorrow."

"Well, at least, Libbie will return with me," his father said.

But Libbie smiled and shook her head, also. "I'm going with Autie," she answered. "I'm always going to follow him wherever he's ordered, if I can. I've made up my mind to that."

CHAPTER XII

The Bugles Call Again

O N A peaceful fall afternoon, a glossy, high-stepping team of bay horses trotted along a street in Monroe, Michigan. Custer was driving them, and beside him in the shining buggy sat Libbie.

After a year at the army post in Texas, Custer had been mustered out of the service. Like most other officers who had served in the war, he had lost his wartime rank when peace was declared. He was now only a captain in the United States Cavalry.

Judge Bacon had died and left Libbie his fortune and his big house. Autie found this comfortable home very pleasant at first, after five years of war and hardship. But Monroe was very quiet.

[*115*]

"Nothing ever seems to happen here," Autie thought as he and Libbie drove down the tree-lined street. "One day is exactly like the last."

With a sigh, he turned to his wife. "The sound of the horses' hoofs on this road makes me think of cavalry on the march," he said. "I might as well confess, Libbie, that I'm just not made for peace and quiet. I'd almost give an arm to lead a regiment of cavalry again and to hear the bugles sounding 'Charge!' "

Libbie loved the safety and quiet of her

home, but she loved her husband more. "If you want a regiment of cavalry and bugles blowing, that's exactly what *I* want for you, too," she told him.

"I've read in the papers that the Indians on the western plains are on the warpath," Custer said. "Troops will be needed to fight against them. Maybe my chance will come before too long."

When they reached home Eliza met them in the doorway. "A boy just brought this telegram for you, General," she announced. Custer would always be "General" to her.

Custer read the telegram quickly and gave a wild whoop of joy. "Listen, Libbie!" he cried. "My chance *has* come. I'm offered a commission as lieutenant colonel in the Seventh Cavalry. It's a new regiment and we'll be stationed at Fort Riley, Kansas, to fight the Indians. Get the atlas, Libbie. Let's find the map of Kansas and see where it is that we're going."

"Are you going to take Miss Libbie out among those heathen savages, General?" Eliza demanded.

"Of course I am! Libbie's my best soldier,"

[*117*]

Custer answered gaily. "And you're coming too, Eliza. You know we can't get along without you. Go hunt up your carpetbag and start packing."

Eliza shook her head disapprovingly. But she hurried to find her bag, nevertheless. "Miss Libbie will need me to stand by her while the general goes sky-hootin' over the country after the Injuns," she said to herself.

Not one of those three, and very few of the American people, bothered to wonder why the Indians had gone on the warpath at this time. The red men had risen to fight against what seemed to them wicked injustice.

When the Civil War had ended, thousands of people had begun to move into the great, unsettled West. New stagecoach routes were mapped out. Railroad tracks were laid farther and farther westward across the plains. The Americans seemed to have forgotten that they had promised not to take that land from the Indians.

Some of the chiefs had traveled to Washington to complain that streams of white men were entering their country.

"You gave us your word that we could keep

[*118*]

our hunting grounds so long as the grass grows and the rivers run," they protested. "Here is the paper you signed."

But the government officials would not help the Indians keep their country. White men were demanding land upon which to farm and build villages and towns.

"The Indians don't use the land wisely, anyway," the officials said, making excuses for their broken promises. "They are wasteful and foolish. Land should belong to civilized people, not to ignorant savages," they declared.

"We will set aside special territory for you, called Indian reservations," the officials told the Indians. "We will send men there called Indian agents, who will watch over you and teach you how to farm and to live like white men. If you obey these agents and stay on your reservations, we will give you plenty of food and blankets. You will be safe and happy."

Some of the Indian tribes agreed to this plan. But most of the proud, fierce, freedom-loving red men would not or could not change their way of life so suddenly. They wanted to hunt buffalo—not to farm.

These Indians of the plains had horses and

[*119*]

they had learned to use rifles. They were dangerous enemies. They raided and burned the white settlers' homes. They attacked stagecoaches and wagon trains, and they killed many white people without mercy.

But many white men treated the red men just as badly. They tricked them and cheated them and were sometimes cruel and savage. Because white men wanted the land at Sand Creek, Colorado, on which an Indian village stood, they attacked the Indians there. After they had killed most of the men, women, and children, they burned the village.

However, the rights and wrongs of these faraway red men meant little to Custer as he made ready to go to Fort Riley in Kansas.

"I'm going out where the bugles call," he thought. "I'm going out to the life of action and adventure that I love!" With Libbie, Eliza, his horses, and his dogs, he set out on his journey westward.

Fort Riley, Kansas, was not a stone-walled fortress, as Libbie had expected. It was nothing but a group of wooden buildings set about a parade ground. Near by were a few workshops, barns for hay, and stables for horses.

They attacked stagecoaches and wagon trains

Beyond, an immense, empty, rolling plain stretched away to the circle of the horizon. There were no trees in sight except a thin line of cottonwoods along a stream near the fort.

The 7th Cavalry was only partly organized when Custer arrived. Most of the soldiers were new to the army and new, too, to this wild western country. Custer had only the winter months in which to get his regiment into shape. General Hancock, who commanded all the troops in this region, planned a campaign in the spring.

"The Cheyennes are making trouble," he told his officers. "We'll take a strong force of infantry, cavalry, and artillery out after them. We'll try to scare them so they'll make peace and settle down on the reservation which has been assigned to them. If they won't, we'll destroy them."

On March 27, Hancock's expedition started from Fort Riley. The 7th Cavalry rode out smartly with harness jingling and pennants snapping in the wind. The band played Custer's favorite tune, "Garry Owen."

At their head rode Colonel Custer. He wore a suit of fringed buckskin like the plainsmen

[*122*]

who served as army scouts. His horse pranced to the music of the band, and Custer waved his white sombrero in a gay farewell to Libbie.

Beside him rode his brother Tom, who was now an officer in the same regiment.

"The Seventh will be a fine fighting outfit some day," Custer said confidently to Tom. He turned in his saddle to look back at the long blue lines trotting briskly behind him. "They'll be the best on the plains—you wait and see! But most of the men need seasoning. They aren't even first-rate riders yet. I hope this expedition will make real cavalrymen out of them."

CHAPTER XIII

Court-Martial!

HANCOCK'S forces marched for almost two weeks over the trackless prairie. They were guided by a famous scout named Wild Bill Hickok, and a group of friendly Indians. On April 9, while they were struggling through a late snowstorm, the scouts brought news that they had sighted a large camp of Cheyennes.

General Hancock sent his Indian runners ahead to ask the Cheyenne chiefs to come and talk with him. But when the runners returned they brought back only excuses.

"The weather is too cold. We are busy hunting buffalo. We will meet you and talk with you later," the chiefs had said.

General Hancock frowned. "I won't stand insolence! Tell them to come at once," he ordered. "And in the meantime, we'll march on. I'll surround their village before they realize what a large force we have."

"General, them Injuns know all about us already, down to the last pack mule," Wild Bill told him. "Their scouts have been watching us for the past thirty miles."

"Is that a fact, Bill?" young Tom Custer asked later. "How do you know? I've been watching out for Indians through my field glasses all along. I haven't seen one."

"Neither have I," Wild Bill answered, grinning. "But I know Injuns."

That evening the Cheyenne messengers brought word that the chiefs would come to talk with General Hancock in the morning. But the morning passed and no chiefs came. At noon, the general marched his troops forward. Soon they saw a crowd of horsemen in the distance riding toward them over the melting snow. Hancock reined in his mount.

"That looks more like a war party than a conference," he said. "But we'll wait and see."

On the Indians came, riding slowly abreast

in long, compact lines. Custer thought there must be at least three hundred of them.

The lean, dark, powerful warriors sat easily on their nimble, half-wild ponies. The wind ruffled the bright feathers of their war bonnets. Hideous war paint of green, white, blue, and scarlet streaked their faces. They carried bows and arrows, lances, and new-looking rifles.

Three chiefs rode out, zigzagging their horses back and forth as they advanced.

"That's the sign of peace. They want to talk," Wild Bill explained.

Hancock and Custer and an interpreter rode ahead to meet them, while the 7th Cavalry waited, alert and ready.

"We want peace," the Indians said, through

the interpreter. "But do not come any nearer to our village. Our women and children are afraid of the bluecoat soldiers."

"Very well. We'll stay here," Hancock agreed. But when he tried to set a time later that day for a conference, the Indians made excuses again.

"Our old-man-chief is not here. He is still out hunting buffalo. He will be back tomorrow, and we will meet you for council tomorrow," they said.

But when morning came, the Indians had all disappeared! The scouts reported that no one was left in the village. Only deserted tepees and cold campfires remained where the busy encampment had stood the day before.

General Hancock was furious. "Burn their tepees down, the tricky brutes! And you go after them, Custer," he ordered. "Round them up and drive them on to the reservation."

This was a difficult task for soldiers who were not used to the plains. The Indians had scattered and their trails led in all directions. Even with Wild Bill for a guide, the 7th Cavalry hunted for two months, but did not find a single Cheyenne.

All that they found were burned stage stations and homesteads, and slaughtered settlers. The Cheyennes had struck like gray wolves, and then vanished.

From time to time the regiment halted at small outposts which were guarded by soldiers. The army kept food and supplies in these outposts. But the food was often scanty and bad.

"This bread was baked in 1861!" a trooper cried, as he pried open a box with a crowbar. "The date's stamped right on it. Nobody could eat that moldy mess."

"And look at this bacon!" another exclaimed. "I'm going to show it to the colonel."

He carried the package to Custer and unwrapped it. Flat stones had been sandwiched in between the rancid, greasy slabs of bacon.

"And the army bought that stuff by the pound!" Tom said in disgust.

Custer's eyes blazed.

"The crook who sold that to the army is worse than any Indian," he said angrily. "If I could get my hands on the man who did it, I'd stuff it down his throat, rocks and all!"

But meanwhile the soldiers had nothing better to eat, unless they took time to go hunt-

[*129*]

ing. And Hancock's orders were still, "Keep after the Cheyennes."

With the coming of summer, heat and thirst were added to their troubles. For weeks they had been forcing their horses over the parched, treeless land. Now the men were worn out and

hungry and began to desert whenever they came near a settlement. Custer caught some of the runaways and punished them. But he could not stop all the desertions.

Late in June a band of Sioux warriors swooped down on the cavalry encampment just before dawn. They tried to surprise the troops and capture their horses. But the soldiers fought them off. This small victory raised their spirits a little.

But when they reached the next outpost, Fort Wallace, they found that a frightful disease called cholera had broken out. Settlers and soldiers alike were dying of it. Medicine and food supplies had been used up, and hostile Indians were destroying every wagon train that tried to get through with more. Starvation and disease together faced the disheartened troopers.

Custer found orders from General Hancock here, too: "Continue after the Cheyennes, using Fort Wallace for a base."

"But, Autie, we can't go on!" Tom protested. "Half our men are sick, and lots of the others are too weak from hunger to ride!"

Custer nodded. He was pacing the narrow room in the fort headquarters. Suddenly he stopped. "Tom, we *must* have medicine and food! I'm going to Fort Harker to get them," he said. "If I sent anyone else through that hostile Indian country he'd have to hide in the daytime and ride at night and he'd be too slow. He might not get there at all. So I'll go myself."

"But General Hancock's orders—" Tom began.

"I know what I've got to do, orders or no orders," Custer answered impatiently. "I'll need seventy-five men and the best horses we have left. That'll be enough to smash through any hostile Indians we meet, and to guard the supply train on the way back. *I'll* make sure it gets back safely!"

It was two hundred and ten miles to Fort Harker, where the railway and telegraph lines began. Custer and his men made the ride in sixty-seven hours. They arrived at midnight and Custer roused the supply sergeant from sleep to order the food and medicines that were needed.

"Is there cholera at Fort Wallace, too?" the sergeant asked. "I hear it's bad at Fort Riley, Colonel."

"At Fort Riley?" Custer echoed. His heart seemed to pause in its beating. Libbie was at Fort Riley!

He hurried to General Smith, who was in command at Fort Harker, and shook him awake.

"Please give me your permission, sir, to go to Fort Riley by train while my supply wagons for Fort Wallace are being loaded," he demanded.

Smith granted the permission and Custer boarded the next train. It seemed like the longest journey of his life. But at the end of it joyful news waited. The rumor of cholera at Fort Riley was a mistake. Libbie was safe and well.

Custer returned to Fort Wallace with his wagons filled with supplies. By the time he reached there, General Hancock had decided to give up his pursuit of the Cheyennes. But Custer had disobeyed orders, no matter what the reason.

General Hancock's aide brought him a message. "You are under arrest," he said. "You are ordered to Fort Leavenworth to await court-martial."

"Court-martial!" Tom cried indignantly. "When you saved your men and the rest of the garrison from cholera and starvation!"

[*133*]

"I knew my orders," Custer answered. "But I made my own decision and acted on it. I think I was right and I'd do the same thing again if I had to. I'll answer for what I did before the court and take the consequences, whatever they are."

But Custer's explanation did not satisfy the judges at his trial. They were not interested, either, in his angry words about the uneatable food which had been supplied for his troops.

"That is not the question before this court," the judges told him. "You disobeyed your orders when you left Fort Wallace." And they found him guilty.

Standing at rigid attention, straight as a steel ramrod, Custer heard his sentence.

"You are suspended from command, rank, and pay for the term of one year."

CHAPTER XIV

A Battle and a Rescue

H ERE'S news of the Seventh Cavalry in to-day's paper, Libbie," Custer exclaimed.

It was a warm afternoon late in September. The Custers were seated on the shady porch of their home in Monroe.

He did not wait for her to reply, but continued eagerly. "General Sheridan's in command now. The Cheyennes are on the warpath again, and Sheridan sent the Seventh out after them under General Sully. It looks as though the Injuns gave Sully a bad licking. And the Seventh's the best regiment on the plains!"

He flung the paper down and began to pace the porch restlessly. "If only I had been there! A whole year out of the army is a long, long time."

"I know it's hard for you, Autie," Libbie said gently. "But try to forget it for a while. We're going to have dinner with Paul and Sally this evening, and I hope you'll enjoy yourself."

An hour later Autie and Libbie were seated among the gay group about their friends' dining table. Custer and his host were deep in plans for a hunting trip when a maid appeared at Custer's elbow.

"This telegram came to your home, General," she said. "Your Eliza brought it over."

Custer tore open the envelope and read the telegram quickly. His face was radiant.

"It's from Sheridan!" he announced. "He has asked the War Department to let me return to duty under him and he wants me to come at once. I'm to command the Seventh Cavalry again, in a campaign against the hostile Cheyennes."

Autie sprang up and pulled Libbie to her feet, too. "Excuse us, Sally. I have to take the next train out, and there's a lot to do."

"May I go with you, Autie?" Libbie asked, when they reached home.

He shook his head. "Not on this trip," he

[136]

said, patting her shoulder. "There won't be time for you to get ready. You understand, don't you, Libbie?"

"Yes," Libbie answered. Because she was a soldier's wife, she managed to smile. But she felt her heart sink. Autie was going into danger again!

Custer arrived at his regiment's headquarters in the Oklahoma Territory early in October. He swiftly set about organizing his men for the campaign.

"Those Cheyennes won't get away this time," he told Lieutenant Cooke, his aide. "I was a greenhorn last year. But now it's going to be different."

On November 23, the 7th Cavalry marched out once again while the band played gaily. Custer's orders from General Sheridan were definite. He was to take his men to the Washita River where the hostile Indians were supposed to be spending the winter.

"Destroy their villages and ponies and kill or hang all warriors and bring back all women and children," Sheridan commanded.

A snowstorm had begun in the night, and snow was still falling heavily.

"Too bad to have such weather when you start," Sheridan commented.

"All the better for us," Custer answered. "It will keep the Indians in their camps. They'll be easier to catch than if they were moving around. And snow muffles noise. We can march quietly."

Soon the driving flakes became so thick that the scouts and guides could not find their way. Then Custer himself led the column, riding with his compass in his hand.

On their third day of marching, the sky cleared. Custer halted his supply wagons. The cavalry was given ammunition for the attack. Then Custer rode ahead with the scouts. The long blue-coated line of horsemen followed the trail they broke through the deep snow.

In the evening they paused for a hot meal, but they did not make camp. Instead, they continued the march through the early winter dusk. They moved as silently as they could, for they were drawing near the Washita River.

By midnight, Hard Robe, one of the friendly Indian scouts, reported that he smelled smoke. Custer halted the column, while he and the guides continued up a tree-crowned ridge.

There in the valley below them lay the Cheyenne camp, dark and silent in the moonlight beside the icy stream.

Hard Robe tugged at Custer's arm. "Heap big village here. Many warriors. Maybe more along the river in the woods," he whispered.

"Don't worry," Custer told him. "We can handle them." The numbers of the enemy he was to attack had never troubled Custer, and they did not now. Returning to his men, he gave swift orders.

"We'll attack at dawn," he directed. He divided his troops into four parts. When the bugle sounded, three sections were to charge into the village on horseback from three different directions. The fourth section, made up of sharpshooters, was to stay on the ridge and fire upon the enemy with their rifles.

The soldiers moved quietly over the moonlit snow to their positions. Tensely they waited while the hours passed.

When the first bright edge of dawn appeared on the eastern horizon, the wild bugle call of "Charge!" shook the frosty air. Then a volley of shots from the sharpshooters crashed into the tepees of the Cheyennes. The yelling troopers dashed down upon the village from three sides. For once, white men had taken Indians completely by surprise.

The Cheyennes fought back with desperate courage, but it was soon over. The chief and most of his warriors lay dead in the snow among the lodges. All the others were taken captive.

Then the tepees and all the Indian property were burned or destroyed. With the prisoners mounted on their own ponies, the regiment rode back in triumph.

When the other Cheyennes heard what had happened to the village on the Washita, some made peace and went to the reservations. Others fled farther into the wilderness but

continued their warfare. Still others went north to join the strong, fierce Sioux.

Custer was kept busy in the months that followed, subduing other hostile tribes and forcing them on to their reservations.

"You've done a good job, Custer," Sheridan told him at last. "Now here's another sort of task for you.

"Some hostile Cheyennes have captured two white women, Mrs. Morgan and Miss White, and taken them to their camp. The brother of one of them, Mr. Daniel Brewster, has learned where they are and has asked me to rescue them. See what you can do."

Custer knew that if he attacked the Indians, they would kill their captives at once. He must use persuasion.

With young Daniel Brewster riding beside him, Custer marched his men toward the place where the Indians were camping. A few miles from the village, advance scouts came suddenly upon three Indian hunters asleep by their fire, and captured them.

"These men are big war chiefs," the scouts said. "Their names are Dull Knife, Big Head, and Fat Bear."

"Give them horses and bring them along," Custer ordered. "But don't let them escape."

When they came in sight of the camp, Custer halted his men. Then he and Lieutenant Cooke advanced alone. They rode their horses in zigzags, signaling that they came in peace and wished to talk.

After a few moments three Indians rode out from the village. They, too, signaled peace.

"So far, so good," Custer said to Cooke. "Come on."

The Cheyennes led them, riding slowly, into the camp. Their chief, Stone Forehead, came out of his tepee and motioned for Custer to dismount and enter. But Lieutenant Cooke was to remain outside.

Stone Forehead gestured for Custer to sit down beside him. Other Indians entered, and soon the tepee was full of scowling braves. After a solemn pause for smoking the peace pipe, Stone Forehead spoke to his interpreter.

"Why has Long Hair come here to the lodges of the Cheyennes?" the interpreter translated.

"I have come in peace to tell you to go to the reservation your white brothers have pre-

"I have come in peace"

pared for you," Custer answered. "And also to get the two white women who are here."

There was a stir among the Indians. "We captured them. They are our prisoners. Why should we give them up?" the chief asked haughtily.

"For three reasons," Custer answered. *"I have three prisoners—Dull Knife, Big Head, and Fat Bear. My men have put ropes around their necks. If you do not return the two white women by sunset, your men will be hanged."*

There was a long silence in the tepee. Indian braves thought hanging was a shameful way to die, as Custer knew well. He knew, also, that he himself was at this moment in the power of these Indians. Nothing could save him if they chose to revenge themselves upon him. He had taken a desperate chance with his own life as the stake. Would his luck hold?

At last Stone Forehead spoke. "Go back to your bluecoat soldiers, Long Hair. We will send the women to you."

Custer and Cooke rode back to their own lines. Anxiously they waited while the hours passed. Would the Indians keep their word, or would they try some trick?

The sun was near the horizon when a trooper gave a shout.

"Here they come!" he cried.

A horse with two riders was crossing the open space between the soldiers and the Indians. Brewster gave a cry of recognition and ran forward. His sister and Miss White were thin and dirty and dressed in rags, but they were safe!

For several years after this campaign, Custer was stationed at other army posts which were not in hostile Indian country. But in 1873, the men who owned the Northern Pacific Railroad decided to lay tracks across territory which was occupied by the Sioux. Surveyors were sent to map the new land. They needed protection from the hostile Indians. Custer and his regiment were given this job.

They rode with the surveyors from Fort Lincoln, in the Dakota Territory, to the Yellowstone River, through wild, unknown country. Lonesome Charley Reynolds and Bloody Knife, an Arikara Indian, were Custer's scouts.

The angry Sioux kept on the heels of the expedition day and night. They swooped down on stragglers and small groups of white men, like wolves circling a herd of buffalo. Their Indian ponies were swift and they were good shots with their rifles.

Lonesome Charley pointed one morning to a group of Indians watching from a hilltop just out of bullet range.

"That one in the lead is Crazy Horse, war chief of the Oglala Sioux," he said.

Custer looked through his field glasses. He could see a slight, sinewy brave on a yellow-spotted pony. The Indian wore a red-backed hawk on his head instead of feathers or a war bonnet.

"He looks like any other Injun buck to me," Custer said.

"Crazy Horse is great warrior," Bloody Knife said earnestly.

"He's a good cavalry leader, too, General," Lonesome Charley added.

Custer laughed aloud. "Perhaps, for an Injun," he said.

CHAPTER XV

Sitting Bull's Dream

THE white men have broken their promise again!" cried Crazy Horse. "They promised that they would keep out of our sacred mountains, the Black Hills. But ever since Long Hair rode through there with his bluecoat soldiers, white men have come pouring in."

"They want to dig for gold and silver," old Chief Red Cloud tried to explain. Several Sioux chiefs were sitting round the fire in his tepee. Red Cloud was friendly with the white men, and he lived with his followers on the reservation.

"We don't use the gold and silver, and the white men like it very much," he continued. "They have asked the chiefs of our nation to meet them in council. They will give us a great price if we will sell the Black Hills to them."

"Sell the Black Hills? Never!" Crazy Horse exclaimed.

Sitting Bull leaned forward. He was the leader of the Hunkpapa Sioux, and very wise in council. "Even if we should sell, who believes that the white men would ever pay us? They do not keep their bargains," he said, in his deep, smooth voice. "I will not deal with the white men. I will not even come to their council. You may tell them that from me, Red Cloud."

Then Sitting Bull and Crazy Horse mounted their ponies and rode northward, and many of the Sioux followed them. Very few chiefs came to the meeting the white men had arranged. There were not enough to make the sale of the Black Hills legal.

The snow fell early that year. It piled in deep drifts all over the prairie. It stalled railroad engines and wagon trains. The Indians who lived on the Sioux reservation grew hungry waiting for the food the white men had promised them.

"You said that if we stayed here you would

give us plenty to eat," they complained to the agent.

"The wagons are bringing it, but the snow is too deep. They can't get through," the agent explained.

Then Sitting Bull sent messengers to the reservation Indians. "Come and eat with me. I have plenty of fat buffalo meat in my kettles. I will not lie to you, as the white men do," the messages said.

Every night after that, groups of Indians silently packed up their tepees and left the reservation. They traveled northward through the snow to join Sitting Bull and his people. His camp was soon the largest in all the Sioux country.

This worried the Indian agents. They asked General Sheridan for help.

"Sitting Bull is a skillful leader and speaker. With so many braves in his camp he'll be stirring up an Indian war, if something isn't done," they told the general.

Sheridan promptly sent a message to Sitting Bull. "Come and live on the reservation and show that you are my friend, like Red Cloud. If you do not, I will know that you are my

[*150*]

enemy. And then I shall send soldiers after you and drive you in."

Sitting Bull received the message in his winter camp. He puffed on his pipe for a long time before he answered.

"I am on my hunting grounds, on land given to my people by the white men in a treaty. I have not sold this land, and I shall not sell it. I shall stay here. The soldiers may come for me if they like. I shall not run away."

When spring had melted the snow, Crazy Horse brought his people to Sitting Bull's village. They traveled together, after that. They hunted the buffalo, moving from one camping place to another as their great pony herds ate up the grass.

Soon afterward, Two Moons, a chief of the Cheyennes, joined them with his followers. The three leaders met one evening in Sitting Bull's tepee. Gall, the Hunkpapa war chief, was there also.

"Do you think that the bluecoat soldiers will really come here?" Two Moons asked. "Or was it only big talk?"

Sitting Bull waved his eagle-feather fan slowly, for the evening was warm. "I think

Crazy Horse brought his people to Sitting Bull's village

they will come," he answered. "But when they see how many warriors we have here, I think they will leave us in peace."

"But if they don't?" Two Moons persisted.

"Then we must fight. There is no other choice," Sitting Bull said. "We are stronger now than we have been for many years. I think we can drive them away. But if we can't, if they kill us all, isn't it better to die in battle than to starve slowly, penned like cattle on the reservations?"

"Yes, that is true," Two Moons answered.

"You are right," Crazy Horse said. "But *I* think that this time we will not be the ones to die. I have been fighting against the white soldiers for a long while, and I have figured out a new way of fighting them."

"A new way?" Two Moons repeated.

"Yes," Crazy Horse continued. "We have learned to shoot straight with their guns. We have plenty of guns now, and plenty of bullets, too. Our horses are better in battle than theirs are. They are swifter and quicker at turning."

"That's so," the others nodded. Their eyes gleamed.

[*153*]

"Now I believe we must use the white man's way of fighting as well as we use his guns," said Crazy Horse. "I have already tried it, even against their big chief, Long Hair, and it works. We must ride all together at the enemy in a great storm of warriors.

"No one must stop in the middle of the battle to take scalps or to do brave deeds all alone. He must stay with the other warriors and fight as planned beforehand."

There was a silence in the shadowy tepee while the others thought this new idea over.

"Do you suppose the braves will be willing to change the ways of their fathers?" Two Moons asked doubtfully.

"Our fathers changed their ways when they first began to catch and ride horses," Sitting Bull reminded him. "They changed again when they learned to use guns instead of bows and arrows. Crazy Horse's medicine is very strong in battle. I think that all of the warriors should listen to his words."

"And your medicine is very strong in council, Sitting Bull," Two Moons said courteously. "I will talk with the Cheyenne warriors and ask them to do as you say."

[*154*]

He stood up, and the three Sioux chiefs followed him out into the summer twilight. Near the tepee Sitting Bull's children were playing. They had made some little horses out of clay from the riverbank and they had tied green leaves over them for saddle blankets.

There was a quiet evening hush over the whole huge encampment. From the willows along the stream came the clear notes of a reed flute. A young brave was courting a girl with music.

"Great camps like this, of all the people,

used to gather years ago. They held their sun dances then in the Greasy Grass Valley beside the river called Little Bighorn," Crazy Horse said. "We shall be camping there soon again. It will be like the old days before the white men came to spoil our hunting grounds."

"Perhaps the white men will not come this time," Gall said.

"We shall see very soon," Sitting Bull answered. "I had a dream. I dreamed of many bluecoat soldiers falling into camp."

Crazy Horse and Gall looked at each other and were silent. The dreams of Sitting Bull were important, for often they foretold the future.

CHAPTER XVI

The Seventh Rides Away

LIBBIE CUSTER sat sewing on the gallery of her husband's quarters at Fort Lincoln, Dakota Territory. It was May, but the sunshine was still chilly. Beside her sat Custer's sister Margaret, who was now married to Lieutenant Jim Calhoun of the 7th Cavalry. Tom Custer and George Yates leaned against the railing with their heads bent over a newspaper.

They could hear the clinking of hammers and the screech of metal against whirling grindstones from the blacksmith's shop beyond the parade ground. These were sounds which Libbie had learned to dread, for they meant that the cavalry was getting ready for battle. The smiths were shoeing the horses.

The wheelwrights were tightening the wheels of the supply wagons. And the troopers were sharpening their sabres.

The 7th Cavalry was preparing to join a great spring campaign to break the power of Sitting Bull and his Sioux once and for all. But there was a strange, listless air about the preparations, for Custer himself was not there. He had been called to Washington two months before, and had not returned.

"I'm afraid Autie's got himself into trouble in Washington," Tom Custer announced, looking up from his paper. "An army general's been accused of dishonesty and Autie's just told some congressmen all that he knows about him."

"But why should that mean trouble for Autie?" Margaret asked. "There's nothing wrong about that."

"The general has powerful friends in the Government," Tom said. "They wanted to keep the story hushed up. But you know Autie. He's not afraid of anyone and he's blurted it all out. It looks as if the general's friends are not going to let Autie go on our expedition."

Libbie's heart gave a bound of hope. Could anyone really keep Autie out of danger? "Autie won't go?" she asked.

"That's the way it seems now," Tom answered. "But here comes your Jim, Margaret. Perhaps he's got some later news."

Young Lieutenant Jim Calhoun came up the steps two at a time. There was a frown on his handsome face.

"What is it, Jim?" Tom demanded. "Are we marching without Autie?"

"No," Calhoun answered. "A telegram's just come saying that he'll be here any day now. But because of the trouble in Washington he's not to be allowed to command the expedition. General Terry will command. Autie'll lead the Seventh, but he'll take his orders from Terry."

Tom scowled. "It's a shame! Terry's a fine officer, but he's had no experience fighting Indians. But look, Jim, there's Captain Keogh on his new horse, Comanche. Let's see if he's heard anything different."

The two young men clattered down the steps in their spurred boots and hurried across the parade ground. Libbie's hope faded. Her husband would ride into danger again, as he had so many times before.

On May tenth Custer arrived at Fort Lincoln with General Terry. At once the whole place sprang to new life. The work went forward briskly under Custer's quick, firm orders. The men moved with a snap and dash they had lacked for months.

Custer was in high spirits. He drew in deep breaths of the bright, clear air.

"It's good to be back after those months cooped up in Washington," he told his wife. "There's nothing like the space and sunlight of these plains. I tell you, Libbie, I'd rather be an ordinary trooper in the cavalry out here than an important officer in the infantry anywhere else in the country!"

Libbie smiled understandingly. When the time came for the expedition to leave, she begged to ride a little way with them.

"Very well," her husband agreed. "You and Margaret may come for the first day's march. I'll send you back with the paymaster."

"The paymaster?" Libbie repeated.

"Yes, tomorrow's pay day. But I don't want the men to spend all their money just before a campaign, so I'm having them paid after they leave," Custer explained. "Then they'll have money to spend when they come back."

"If they *do* come back," Libbie almost said aloud, but she stopped herself just in time.

Early, before the sun rose on May 17, the infantry and field artillery started from the fort. Next, the wagon train of supplies creaked into motion and rolled out through the misty dawn. At seven the bugles blew the order, "Mount!" and the six hundred waiting troopers swung into their saddles. The band struck up "Garry Owen." The march had begun.

Lonesome Charley, Bloody Knife, and twenty-five friendly Arikara Indians rode with the soldiers as scouts. The regiment circled out past the Arikara camp on the outskirts of the fort. Suddenly the squaws and old men who were left behind set up a strange, wailing chant. The Indian scouts echoed it as they rode by, beating time on the small war drums they carried.

Libbie was riding with Custer at the head of the column, and she turned in her saddle to look back.

"How mournful that sounds!" she exclaimed. "Do the warriors always sing like that when they are leaving camp?"

Lonesome Charley shook his head. "Only when they are going into a great battle," he said. "These Arikaras know that they are riding against the Sioux, and they have a great respect for the way the Sioux can fight."

Libbie glanced at her husband in alarm, but his quick smile reassured her.

"Don't worry, Libbie," he said. "The Seventh Cavalry could lick all the Indians on the plains if it had to. But what this expedition is going to do is just to give the Sioux a scare they'll never get over.

"General Crook, with over a thousand men, is coming up from the south. General Gibbon

and his troops are on the Yellowstone River now, and they will be ready on the north. Our allies, the Crow Indians, will be waiting on the west. And we'll drive in from the east.

"When the Sioux learn that they are surrounded they'll give in soon enough. Then we'll herd them onto their reservation. There probably won't be any real fighting at all."

Lonesome Charley's face was grave, and he kept silence. But Libbie was not looking at him. She saw only Custer's gay, confident grin and the glow in his blue eyes.

"He has always returned safely," she told herself. "They call it 'Custer Luck.' I'll remember that and not spoil this extra day we have together."

And so it was a cheerful family party that camped that night near the soldiers' bivouac. Libbie, Margaret, Tom Custer, Jim Calhoun, and George Yates were there. So were Boston Custer and Lydia's young son, Armstrong Reed, also. The two boys had just arrived from the East and were wild with delight because they had been allowed to come along. There was talk and laughter around the campfire until late at night.

But morning came at last. Libbie and Margaret mounted and prepared to return to the fort with the paymaster, while the regiment started forward again.

Custer was riding his bright sorrel, Vic. His fringed buckskin suit was new, almost yellow in the sun, and his scarlet neckerchief blew in the wind. He wore his hair short, clipped off with horse clippers, as usual before a campaign.

He had never looked more vigorous and gallant than he did on that morning as he rode off at the head of the long, blue column. Libbie reined in her horse and sat watching the golden horse and golden rider until they disappeared over a small hill.

She was to cherish that picture in her mind all the rest of her life. For that was the last sight she ever had of her husband.

CHAPTER XVII

Custer's Last Fight

SLOWLY General Terry's army toiled over the rough, sun-parched miles toward the Yellowstone River. When they came to the jumbled canyons of the "Badlands," even the Indian guides admitted that they were lost. But Custer was always able to find the way, and he led the column safely through the trackless wilderness.

They met General Gibbon and his soldiers near the place where the muddy Powder River empties into the Yellowstone. Here Terry halted his whole army and set up camp to rest and prepare for the final roundup of the Sioux.

Gibbon had news. "My scouts report that a large band of Sioux is traveling along one of the other rivers that flow north to the Yellowstone," he told Terry and Custer. "It's either the Tongue, the Rosebud, or the Bighorn."

"Have you heard from General Crook?" Terry asked.

Gibbon shook his head.

"He was supposed to start north toward the Yellowstone on May twenty-ninth," General Terry said, with a worried frown. "Well, we'll have word from him before long."

Soon news came from another scouting party. Custer had sent Major Reno, with part of the 7th Cavalry, off westward to look for Indians. On June 19, a dust-covered messenger rode into camp.

"Major Reno's found a fresh Indian trail, a mighty big one," he reported to Custer and the other officers. "It leads west over the Wolf Mountains toward the valley of the Little Bighorn River."

General Terry spread out a map and made his plans quickly. "Custer, you are to take your regiment and follow the trail Reno discovered. When you find the Sioux, prepare to attack from the east," he directed. "General Crook will be near enough by that time to guard against their escape to the south.

"Meanwhile, General Gibbon, you march your infantry and artillery south, up the Big-horn River from its mouth on the Yellow-stone. I will go with your column. But we'll leave enough troops and artillery to patrol the Yellowstone River so that the Sioux can't cross it. On the west our allies, the Crows, will be ready to hold them back.

"I'll set the date for our attack," Terry continued. "Monday morning, June twenty-sixth. That will be our day. It will give us all plenty of time to get set and make ready."

The three officers bending so intently over the maps could not know that part of their plan had failed already. On June 17, General Crook had met Crazy Horse and his Sioux warriors on the distant headwaters of the Rosebud River. The Indians had charged in solid masses straight into the blue lines. They had used Crazy Horse's new way of fighting, and they had won the victory. Crook and his men were driven back. He was still far to the south, waiting for reinforcements before he dared to march north again.

As for the Sioux, they had returned to Sitting Bull's camp wild with triumph.

[*169*]

"Hoka-hey! Crazy Horse has the strongest war medicine in the world!" they chanted. "We will follow him and do his commands always. His medicine is good. *Hoka-hey! Hoka-hey!"*

As soon as Major Reno and his scouting force returned to the camp on the Yellowstone, the whole 7th Cavalry was ready to move. On June 22 they marched. Terry and Gibbon watched from their horses while the mounted squadrons filed past them. The sky was covered with gray clouds. A sharp wind bent the sagebrush, whipped the pennants, and blew the dust away from the horses' hoofs. The men rode smartly and the officers saluted as they passed General Terry.

Custer dashed up at a gallop, reined in his horse suddenly before the general, and saluted with his drawn sabre.

"Good-by and good luck to you, Custer," Terry called. "We'll meet on Monday."

"And wait for us, Custer. Don't be greedy and gobble up all the Sioux before we get there," Gibbon added.

Custer threw back his head and laughed. "I won't," he answered. Then he saluted again and spurred to the head of the line. The Seventh was riding out to battle once more!

Custer and his men soon found the trail Reno had discovered. They followed it for three days. By the morning of June 25 it had

led them to a ridge of the Wolf Mountains above the valley of the Little Bighorn. There the Indian trail was broad and fresh. It wound over the rise and down the slope beyond.

Some of the scouts climbed a peak overlooking the river valley. They were pointing at something and exclaiming when Custer and Tom and Bloody Knife joined them.

"What do you see?" Custer asked.

"Many ponies. Big village. *Too* many Sioux!" the Arikaras were jabbering with excitement.

Custer saw fear on all the dark faces. He stared down into the valley. It was full of morning mist. All he could see were the shining curves of the river winding away to the north. Even with his field glasses he could make out only a vague, dark blur where the Indians pointed.

"There isn't any village there," he said scornfully. "You're looking at trees. The Sioux have got you so scared you can't even see straight."

Bloody Knife shook his head. *"Too* many Sioux," he insisted stubbornly.

"I think they're farther west, beyond those

hills across the next valley," Custer said. "But we'll go down and take a look, anyway."

"But how about Terry and Gibbon?" Tom said uneasily. "This is only the twenty-fifth of June, not the twenty-sixth."

"We can't sit around waiting for the infantry to get here," Custer said. "The Sioux are on the move and they'll run away from us if we don't keep right up with them."

"The Sioux won't run away," Lonesome Charley said. "I visited Sitting Bull last winter. His Sioux are going to stand and fight."

Custer clapped the quiet little scout on the shoulder. "You listened too long to that old Injun spellbinder, Charley," he said. "Sitting Bull hasn't got the Seventh Cavalry to fight for him!"

"No, but he's got Crazy Horse," Lonesome Charley answered.

But Custer was already striding down the rocky slope to where his horse waited for him. As he was mounting, a sergeant came spurring up with news. He had seen a small group of Sioux Indians in the rear of the regiment.

"That settles it," Custer said. "They know about us already. There's no time to lose."

He gave rapid orders. The cavalrymen swung into line and started down the ridge. When they reached the valley Custer called his senior captain.

"Captain Benteen, take your men on over those hills beyond this valley and see if there are Indians there," he directed.

Benteen and his men turned off toward the hills. Custer and the others continued down the valley at a swift trot. Already the pack mules, loaded with ammunition and supplies, were far behind.

One of the scouts rode up a little knoll along the way. He gave a shout. "Indians! There go your Indians on the run. About forty Sioux braves riding ahead of you toward the Little Bighorn River."

"Major Reno, take your men, ford the river, and go after those Indians," Custer called. "I'll be right behind you with the whole outfit."

Reno and his horsemen splashed through the clear flowing water. They formed ranks on the other side and headed down the valley toward a dust cloud which marked where the Indians were riding.

Reno looked back just before a clump of

trees hid the ford from his sight. Custer and his men were not following him across the river. Why not?

No one knows for certain, even now. For some reason, as he had often done before, Custer had quickly changed his plan. Perhaps he had decided to cross the river farther downstream and attack the Indians there. But nobody will ever know.

One of Reno's men glanced across the valley as he rode after the Indians. He saw blue-clad troopers galloping northward along the top of a ridge parallel to the river. Another saw a figure in bright buckskins rein his horse high on a bluff and wave his hat. Then he was gone. And that was the last that any surviving white man ever saw of Custer alive.

Two days later, Terry and Gibbon, with their soldiers, reached the valley of the Little Bighorn. Some terrified Crow Indians had met them with news which they could not believe.

"Long Hair and all his men are dead. The Sioux have killed them all in a great battle," the Crows said.

Terry and his men hurried forward. The

valley of the Little Bighorn lay silent and empty under the hot summer sun. The grass was blackened and burned along the flat land on either side of the river.

Custer had faced death fearlessly many times before.

No Indians were in sight, but the soldiers found traces of the greatest Indian camp any man of them had ever seen. It stretched for more than three miles along the stream,

He met it bravely at the end.

marked by the sites of over two thousand tepees.

Where one lodge had stood were some little horses made of clay. Tied on them, for saddle blankets, were twenty-dollar bills. "The cavalrymen's pay!" an officer exclaimed. "Indian children must have picked them up somewhere to use for their toys!"

Suddenly came the sound of hoarse, feeble shouts, and shots fired in rapid succession—signals. On a ridge above the valley a few blue-clad figures yelled and waved wildly.

Reno and Benteen and what was left of their troops were entrenched there. Fifty-seven men were dead, among them Bloody Knife and Lonesome Charley. Fifty-two were wounded.

They had been beaten and surrounded and held at bay by great hordes of Sioux. The last of the Indians had only left when the soldiers came in sight.

"Where is Custer?" Benteen and Reno and Terry asked in almost the same breath.

Then Terry's men found Custer, too. He lay dead on a hillside about three miles down the stream. So did his two brothers, and his brother-in-law, and also his young nephew. Around him were scattered the two hundred and twelve men of the 7th Cavalry who had followed him. They had fought to the last, but Sitting Bull's warriors, led by Crazy Horse, had overwhelmed and killed them all.

Captain Keogh's horse, Comanche, was the only survivor of Custer's last fight. The horse was still alive in spite of twenty-eight wounds.

"Take care of him, poor fellow," Terry said. "If only he could tell us what happened!"

But every man there knew one thing, at least, for certain. Custer had faced death fearlessly many times before. He met it bravely at the end.

The Sioux had won their victory and moved on over the mountains. But the blow which struck down Custer doomed them also.

From that day on, the whole nation's wrath was kindled against them. They were hunted and scattered and driven until their fighting spirit was broken forever.

Custer's last battle brought final peace to the Western plains he had loved.

[*179*]

About the Author

Margaret Leighton was born in Ohio, but she spent her childhood in Cambridge, Massachusetts. Her father was a college professor and he liked to take his family traveling. One of her earliest memories is of a summer vacation, when she was five, spent at the foot of a huge, towering old castle in Germany, full of legends of princesses, knights, and dragons. She traveled through our own great West, too. And when Margaret Leighton's own four children were old enough, she took them to spend a glorious summer on a Western ranch. Now she lives in a big old house covered with vines high on a cliff above the surf of the blue Pacific. Her garden is full of flowers and trees and birds and, of course, children.

About the Artist

From the time Nick Eggenhofer started to read, as a youngster in Bavaria, Germany, tales of the Western range fascinated him. On arriving in the United States, he worked in New York as a laborer, shoe clerk, machinist, and lithographer. Evenings, he studied at Cooper Union. But when his day's work was done, he painted watercolors of cowboys— for fun. A publisher bought them all, and asked him to illustrate magazine stories of the West. To gather cowboy lore, he made many trips to the far West, and brought back a treasure trove of saddles, bridles, ten-gallon hats, and rifles. He and his wife and daughter now live in New Jersey.

1 *Born in New Rumley, Harrison County, Ohio, December 5, 1839*

2 *Becomes a cadet in the U. S. Militar Academy, West Point, N. Y., 185*

3 *Enters the Civil War as a second lieutenant in the Union Army, 1861*

4 *Leads his first cavalry charge, near Catlett's Station, Virginia, 1862*

10 *Dies fighting Sioux Indians, by the Little Big Horn River, Montana, June 25, 1876*

9 *Rescues two women held prisoners by Cheyenne Indians, 1869*